*A PARENT'S GUIDE TO THE*

# NEW MATHEMATICS

# A PARENT'S GUIDE TO THE

# NEW MATHEMATICS

*by Evelyn Sharp*

*Preface by* HARRY D. RUDERMAN

E. P. DUTTON & CO., INC.
NEW YORK     1964

COPYRIGHTS FROM WHICH PERMISSION TO QUOTE
HAS BEEN GRANTED:

Evelyn Sharp, "The New Math," *The Saturday Review* (January 19, 1963), reprinted by permission
of *The Saturday Review*.

Patrick Suppes, *Sets and Numbers,* Book I (Stanford University Press, 1960; L. W. Singer Company, 1962; © Patrick Suppes, 1960), page 35 of
Stanford edition reprinted by permission of the
author.

Published simultaneously in Canada by Clarke, Irwin
& Company, Limited, Toronto and Vancouver

Library of Congress Catalog Card No. 64–11065

# Preface

Now that the "new math" is being introduced into school curriculums all over the country at almost every grade level, there is a real need for such a book as Evelyn Sharp has written which explains to parents what this new mathematics is and why the traditional program which most parents followed is no longer adequate for today's youngsters. Evelyn Sharp, herself one of the mathematics teachers responsible for guiding children through these new mathematics concepts, has a sympathetic understanding of the average parent's bewilderment and an uncommonly clear way of explaining what these new concepts in mathematics are. As one high school principal wrote, on reading her article, "The New Math: You Don't Count on Your Fingers Any More" (*Saturday Review,* January 19, 1963): "We would like to have all of our school patrons read the article 'New Math' by Evelyn Sharp. . . . The article would be particularly helpful to us for two reasons. First, a number of relatively technical concepts have been so stated that communication can be established with a lay reader. Second, we have established a modern mathematics curriculum in our school from grade three through grade nine, and interpretation of the program, understandably, is a continuing need."

*A Parent's Guide to the New Mathematics* points up the fact that one of the essentials of the schools' new mathematics program is the tremendous emphasis on having children understand clearly the basic principles which underlie mathematics before being asked to figure out mathematical problems. This means that, starting with a firm and meaningful foundation, children should be able to move forward in mathematics with a high level of interest and a genuine feeling of self-reliance.

Mathematics is only one of the fields where the explosive growth of information has pressed educators to extract only the most significant ideas, attitudes, and facts for teaching. In this field, the schools are most fortunate in having had the aid of top mathematicians, many of them of research caliber, to help decide what principles the children should learn, at what age, and, even more important, they have helped in the preparation of the teaching materials. Although the decisions made were often not unanimous, there is no quarrel with the improvement in the quality of the math programs which are now being offered.

But it is vital that parents, too, should appreciate the need for the introduction of these "new math" principles and understand what they are and how and why they differ from their own old-fashioned mathematics training. This is what Evelyn Sharp has done in this excellent introductory book.

HARRY D. RUDERMAN

Chairman, Mathematics Department

*Hunter College High School*
*New York, N.Y.*

# CONTENTS

*A PARENT'S GUIDE TO THE*

# NEW MATHEMATICS

# *The Mathematics Revolution* 1

If you have a child in school you are beginning to feel the impact of a change in mathematics—a change so far-reaching that it warrants the word revolution. Not only has the whole program been revamped and accelerated, but some of the subject matter itself is new. Do you know what Boolean algebra is? Or non-Euclidean geometry?

The opening salvo in the nationwide attack on old-style mathematics was fired in the summer of 1955 when a commission appointed by the College Entrance Examination Board met to discuss a revision of the high school courses in that subject. It was high time.

The general feeling of the commission members was that the standard curriculum was outmoded and that it was based on a static concept of mathematics which was now antiquated. As Dr. Albert E. Meder, Jr., the executive director of the commission, said: If you dug up an old seventeenth-century don he could walk right into any classroom and start teaching math. Nobody would notice the difference, since the content of the courses hadn't changed in the last 300 years.

Furthermore, mathematics was the only subject of which this was true. The don couldn't teach history because he wouldn't know what had happened since the reign of William and Mary. In science he would obviously be lost. He couldn't teach English because we don't speak exactly the same tongue now as then—many words have different meanings. French, Spanish, or any other modern language would be ruled out for the same reason. But in mathematics he would be right at home.

It was a surprise to many people that there was anything wrong with a static mathematics program. If they thought about it at all, they assumed that mathematics was invented in antiquity by Euclid and a few others, added to by such geniuses as Sir Isaac Newton, and given the final touches some time before the battle of Bunker Hill.

Actually, by 1955 mathematics had changed just as much as physics, chemistry, or biology, but not many were aware of it. Why? Because higher mathematics is an esoteric subject, and only the initiated—namely, those who got as far as graduate school—knew what was going on. And few of the initiated taught below college level.

In short, the high school curriculum had lagged far behind the advances in the subject. It was the purpose of the commission to modernize it. They studied the situation for nearly three years, and in 1959 published a report of their recommendations. In essence, it said to cut out obsolete material, regroup the rest, and add the new. Specifically, the report gave the ax to most of solid geometry and to a portion of the traditional course in trigonometry, especially the extensive work on logarithms—a rapid calculating device of the seventeenth century, replaced now by electronic computers. They favored the addition of classes in probability, a subject that deals with the application of mathematics to events in which luck plays a role, and in modern (abstract) algebra.

The commission also published a series of pamphlets to help schools begin the transition, and a textbook which they had written for the course in probability. (There was none available at the high school level.)

To whip up interest Dr. Meder traveled about the country speaking to groups of teachers; he offered to go wherever he could be assured of an audience. The desire for a change had been given a powerful impetus by the launching of the first Sputnik in the fall of 1957.

In the meantime two universities had set up projects of their own. The University of Illinois was already sponsoring experimental classes in a new mathematics curriculum in a dozen high schools in the Midwest, using materials they had developed, and the University of Maryland did the same thing for junior high schools in the Washington area. Both received funds from the Carnegie Corporation of New York, as did the College Board commission.

The next big push came with the creation of the School Mathematics Study Group, an organization including both teachers and representatives of industry—a sort of cross section of the mathematical profession, financed by the National Science Foundation. They took up where the College Board commission left off.

First, in two summer writing sessions in 1958 and 1959, they drafted tentative textbooks for all four years of high school mathematics, in general agreeing with the recommendations of the earlier commission. Then, since mathematics is a subject in which each block must, of necessity, fit on top of the one below it, they undertook a revision of the junior high school curriculum. This in turn called for a change in the sixth-grade course, then the fifth, and so on. Eventually their textbooks reached as far down as the fourth grade, and they are at present engaged in working out material for children younger than that.

To try out their sample texts, the SMSG set up a nationwide network of experiment centers, each a nucleus for experimental classes in some of the schools in that area. The results of this trial teaching were funneled back through the center chairman and evaluated, then used in revising the texts and tried on more classes the following year. To escape the stigma of guinea-pigdom, children were encouraged to feel that they were taking part in a research project and were asked to help answer questions such as: "Are the books well worded?"

It was the large number of these experimental classes which brought the mathematics revolution down to grass roots, for, while the College Entrance Examination Board is the lodestar of those who work with college preparatory groups, the SMSG program reached all kinds of schools.

It was not the intention of the School Mathematics Study Group to enter into the commercial textbook field. In fact, since they had the financial backing of the national government, they could not. Rather, they served as a sort of pioneer footbridge across the gap between traditional and new mathematics until the established publishers could prepare their own series based on the commission's report.

There were also a number of other revision groups. To name a few: the Ball State Program, the Madison Project, the Greater Cleveland Mathematics Program, and the

Boston College Mathematics Institute. All had a similar goal, but there are certain distinguishing features among them. For instance, the Educational Research Council of Greater Cleveland started with the kindergarten and worked up, instead of from the top down, as the SMSG had done. The Madison Project, centered jointly at Syracuse University and Webster College, is not bent on developing textbooks, grade by grade, but suggest that their materials, mostly films and tape recordings, be used to supplement the regular curriculum.

The net result of all these changes has been to speed up a slow, glacierlike movement in mathematics that, for a long time, has been pushing each subject down to an ever earlier level. A century ago geometry was exclusively a college course. Twenty-five years ago so was trigonometry, although more recently it has been taught in both places, a wasteful duplication. Now it may be moved almost entirely into high school—many colleges are doing away with their traditional freshman course of trig and college algebra.

It won't be long until calculus follows them down, shoving everything still another year ahead. Beginning algebra, already presented in the eighth grade for accelerated students, may go even earlier, and arithmetic will be telescoped into elementary school. Old landmarks, like the multiplication tables, fractions, and decimals will all move correspondingly.

This is going to put it up to you, Father, when your child brings you his homework. (Nine times out of ten it is Father who helps with the math. If Mother can also explain the problems, the child is usually so smart he doesn't need help, anyway.) You have two choices. You can take the textbook and, prudently keeping a few lessons in advance, sit down and learn it. Or you can wash your hands of the whole thing, privately agreeing with a little girl I know who said, when she heard about the avalanche of math that was coming: "Gee, I got out of grade school just in time."

# *Sets* 2

What is the new mathematics like? At its core is the set concept, an idea at once so simple that it can be included in the first-grade course of study and so all-pervading that you can't understand modern mathematics without it.

A set is just what you think it is: a group of things that are considered together in some way. You can speak of a set of chairs, a set of people, or a set of numbers. If you look on this _____ as just a line, you may be dreadfully old-fashioned. It's an illustration of a set of points.

For the student, sets offer clarity, simplification, and a method of unifying diverse fragments of knowledge. This single thread runs through arithmetic, algebra, geometry, and such new branches of higher mathematics as topology.

Since each new mathematical idea which the pupils meet relates to the set concept, it is taught at every grade level. In the primary department their sets consist mostly of baby chickens and bunny rabbits and such. High school seniors may deal with sets of vectors. In the grades in between, it is usually collections of numbers or geometrical points that they study.

One of the applications of set theory is in Boolean algebra, so named for George Boole, an English mathemati-

$$\left\{ \triangle \right\} \cup \left\{ \text{🐤} \right\} =$$

☐ $\left\{ \triangle \right\}$      ☐ $\left\{ \text{🐤} \right\}$      ☒ $\left\{ \triangle \ \text{🐤} \right\}$

---

$$\left\{ \text{🐕} \right\} \cup \left\{ \text{🏉} \right\} =$$

☐ $\left\{ \text{🐕} \right\}$      ☐ $\left\{ \text{🐕} \ \text{🏉} \right\}$      ☐ $\left\{ \text{🏉} \right\}$

---

$$\left\{ \text{🦒} \right\} \cup \left\{ \ \ \right\} =$$

☐ $\left\{ \text{🤡} \right\}$      ☐ $\left\{ \text{🦒} \right\}$      ☐ $\left\{ \text{🦒} \ \text{🤡} \right\}$

From Patrick Suppes, *Sets and Numbers*, Book I (Stanford University Press, 1960) p. 35.

cian who pioneered in the study of symbolic logic. It has
been useful in the development of high-speed electronic
digital computers—the electronic brains—where it provides a tangible and workable method of analyzing the
myriad electric circuits involved. Actually, Boolean algebra had been lying around in the attic of pure mathematics for about a century (George Boole died before Abra-
ham Lincoln did) until the dictates of the machines
brought it downstairs.

## Equivalent Sets

Sets are equivalent if they each have the same number
of objects. It is not necessary to know how to count to recognize this. The first-grade book of the Greater Cleveland
Mathematics Program shows a picture of two monkeys
and two bananas, with directions to match them one-to-
one, meaning give a banana to each monkey. (This is a
simplified version of the more sophisticated term "one-to-
one correspondence" used in the higher grades.) No re-
semblance between the objects in the different sets is im-
plied. They are alike only in their twoness.

If you had enough pictures, each showing a different
number of monkeys, and only one showing a collection of
bananas, you could hunt around until you found a monkey set that matched the set of bananas. Even a savage or
a small child could do this. It is an intuitive concept and
has nothing to do with knowing the names of the numbers
or, really, in what order they come. Arranging them in
order is the second step. In such a way all of mathematics
can be built up.

The occurrence of the phrases "Match one-to-one" and "Union of sets" in their books shows that set language is being carried all the way down to the first grade. Use of this basic vocabulary is essential in advancing from one level of achievement to the next. The purpose of introducing it in the early grades is part of the larger purpose of introducing the new mathematics in elementary school: to clarify certain topics included in the traditional arithmetic program, and to make the further study of new topics at higher grade levels easier.

### Set Membership

A set can contain any number of members, from zero on up. If I speak of the set of all the red-haired people in this block and it happens that everybody in the neighborhood is either blond or brunette, that's still all right—I have an empty set and its symbol is $\phi$. This is not as whimsical as it seems. An empty box is not the same as no box at all. The empty set (also called "null set") is simply the set that has no elements.

Membership in a set is denoted by $\epsilon$, the Greek letter epsilon. If you have a set of dogs, $K$ (sets are often named by capital letters), then Rover $\epsilon$ $K$. This is read: "Rover is an element of set $K$," or "Rover is a member of set $K$." If there is a flea on one of the dogs, the flea is not a member of the set. True, he is *there*, but he is not a member—he is an interloper. This would be indicated by writing: flea $\notin$ $K$.

Notice $K$ is not the set of *all* dogs, just the ones in some specific category—maybe those you see out your window. Write it:

$$K = \{\text{Rover, Fido, Lassie}\}$$

This works fine for a small number, but suppose you want to make a set of all the dogs in the Kennel Club show. It would be extremely tedious and impractical to list them by the roster method. The set of all the dogs in the United States would be downright impossible to write that way. Instead, a large set is described by setting down the rule for membership.

$$K = \{\text{all the dogs in the U.S.}\}$$

More properly, it's given this way:

$$K = \{\; x \mid x \text{ is a dog in the U.S.}\}$$

In mathematical jargon this is read: "The set of all $x$ such that $x$ is a dog in the United States." The vertical bar $\mid$ is translated: "such that."

PROBLEMS

1. List the members of the following set:

$$A = \{x \mid x \text{ is an odd number between 0 and 10}\}$$

2. Write the following set by the rule method:

$$A = \{\text{Sunday, Monday, Tuesday, Wednesday, Thursday,}$$
$$\text{Friday, Saturday}\}$$

3. Write the set of all major-league baseball players whose batting average is above .500.

4. What is the name of the figure described in this set?

$$A = \{\text{all points in a plane 2 inches from a given point}\}$$

## SUBSETS

Just as committees have subcommittees, sets have subsets. Starting with $X = \{1,2,3\}$ I can pick any elements of the set I like for a subset—$\{1\}$, or $\{2,3\}$ or $\{3\}$, etc. By convention, every set is a subset of itself, that is $\{1,2,3\}$ is a subset of set $X$. This is stretching a point, but that's the way it is done to achieve consistency.

The null set is also a subset of every set. This is logical if you consider that I might be finicky when I am choosing the members to make a subset and not choose any of them. Then I would have an empty set, but it is still counted as a legal subset.

There is a short-cut way of predicting how many subsets there will be in the bureaucracy. In the example above, I predict there will be eight. Listing them, there are $\{1\}$, $\{2\}$, $\{3\}$, $\{1,2\}$, $\{1,3\}$, $\{2,3\}$, $\{1,2,3\}$, $\phi$. How did I know? I cubed 2, that is took $2 \times 2 \times 2$, which is eight—cubed because the original set had three members. In the set $\{3,5,7,9\}$ I predict there will be sixteen, or 2 raised to the fourth power. Write all the possibilities down and count them if you don't believe me. It works every time. In general, the number of subsets is $2^n$, $n$ being the number of elements of the original set.

To indicate that one set is a subset of another, you use the symbol $A \subset B$, read: "$A$ is a subset of $B$," or "$A$ is contained in $B$." $B \supset A$ says the same thing in reverse order, that is: "$B$ contains $A$."

## PROBLEMS

In problems 1, 2, and 3 let set $A$ consist of one coin of each denomination, U.S. currency, in use at the present time.

1. How many subsets are there of set *A*?
2. How many of these subsets each have an aggregate value of 60 cents or more?
3. How many of these subsets are composed entirely of silver coins?
4. Write the eight subsets of the set {*x,y,z*}

Is each of the following statements true or false?

5. If $A \subset B$ and $B \subset A$, then $A = B$
6. If $A \subset B$ and $B \supset A$, then $A = B$
7. If $A \subset B$ and $B \subset C$ and $C \subset A$, then $B = C$

## SET OPERATIONS

You don't add, subtract, multiply, or divide sets—instead, there are three fundamental operations called intersection, union, and complementation. For an example, you might begin by listing the four-legged objects in the room where you're sitting—say the sofa, the table, an armchair, and the dog. Enclose the list in braces (never parentheses or brackets, always braces) and call it set *A*.

$$A = \{\text{sofa, table, chair, dog}\}$$

Set *B* could be all the animate objects in the room—yourself, the dog, and whoever else happens to be there.

$$B = \{\text{you, dog, John, Sue}\}$$

Now the intersection of sets *A* and *B* would be the dog —he is the only one that fits both categories. In other words, he's a member of both sets. This is written:

$$A \cap B = \{\text{dog}\}$$

$\cap$ is the symbol for intersection.

$A \cap B$ is read: "the intersection of *A* and *B*" or "*A* cap

*B.*" Of course, if you don't have a dog, or even a cat, the intersection would be an empty set, written $A \cap B = \phi$.

The set operations are usually illustrated by drawings, called Venn diagrams after the English logician who popularized them. A Venn diagram of the problem above looks like this:

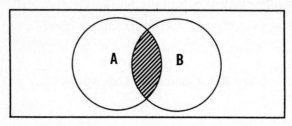

The interior of Circle $A$ represents set $A$; the interior of circle $B$ is set $B$. (They show the relationship between the sets—not their comparative sizes.) The shaded portion is $A \cap B$.

If the intersection is the empty set, then the circles do not overlap. In that case sets $A$ and $B$ are said to be disjoint.

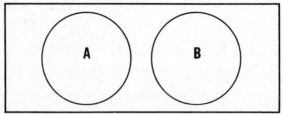

Turn $\cap$ upside down, and you have $\cup$, the symbol for union. $A \cup B$, read: "the union of $A$ and $B$," or "$A$ cup $B$," means all the objects contained in either set.

$$A \cup B = \{\text{sofa, table, chair, dog, you, John, Sue}\}$$

You notice you don't list the dog twice—only once. In Venn diagrams the entire shaded area represents $A \cup B$.

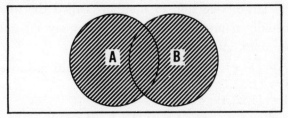

For complementation you need a set and a subset. Say set $V$ comprises all the things you had for dinner:

$V$ = {steak, baked potato, green beans, salad, bread, coffee, apricot mousse}

Then let subset $A$ be only those you had as a first course:

$A$ = {steak, baked potato, green beans, bread}

The complement of set $A$, written $A'$, would be all the other things—the ones you did not have in the first course:

$A'$ = {salad, coffee, apricot mousse}

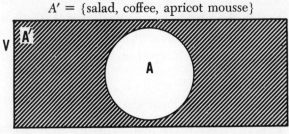

Unfortunately, the symbolism is not yet uniform. I am looking at three books—one uses $A'$, one uses a tilde $\sim A$, and one uses $\bar{A}$ for the complement. Like the man who never knew what time it was because he had two watches, you will be better off if you pick one—the one in your child's textbook—and stick to it.

While sets may contain anything, in arithmetic they are most often numbers. For a sample problem, start with a fairly large collection of numbers called the universal set (usually named $U$, but some books say $V$) and two smaller ones, $A$ and $B$.

$U = \{x \mid x$ is a whole number from 1 to 10, inclusive$\}$
$A = \{1,3,5,7\}$
$B = \{1,2,3,4\}$

The directions might say: "Write the following sets by the listing method:"

1. $A \cup B$     The solution is: $A \cup B = \{1,2,3,4,5,7\}$
2. $A \cap B$     This would be: $A \cap B = \{1,3\}$
3. $A'$     This is: $A' = \{2,4,6,8,9,10\}$
4. $(A \cup B)'$     Worked out: $A \cup B = \{1,2,3,4,5,7\}$
   Therefore the complement is all the other numbers in the universal set or
   $(A \cup B)' = \{6,8,9,10\}$

A page of problems in Boolean algebra looks as if you had scratched them in the ground down by the stables and a sharply shod horse had walked over it. With horseshoes going north, south, east, and west it makes you think of that man who jumped on his mount and rode off in all directions.

### PROBLEMS

LET: $U = \{x \mid x$ is a whole number from 1 to 10, inclusive$\}$
$A = \{2,4,6\}$
$B = \{4,5,6,7\}$
$C = \{3,9,10\}$

For problems 1 through 7, use the universal set and the subsets $A$, $B$, $C$ given above.

Write the following sets by the listing method:

1. $A \cap B$
2. $B \cup C$
3. $B'$
4. $(A \cap B) \cup C$
5. $(A \cup B)'$
6. $(B \cup C)' \cap A$
7. $A \cap C$

Given: $A = \{$all points on straight line $L\}$
$\quad\quad\ B = \{$all points on straight line $M\}$

8. If line $L$ and line $M$ intersect, how many members in set $A \cap B$?
9. If lines $L$ and $M$ are parallel, how many members in set $A \cap B$?
10. What symbol would you use for the set described in exercise 9?

Is each of these statements true or false?

11. $(A \cap B) \subset A$
12. $A \subset (A \cup B)$


## CARTESIAN PRODUCT

The notion of an ordered pair runs through much of mathematics and is the key to understanding many concepts. It means, simply, that the order in which a pair is named makes a difference. $(4, 5)$ is not the same as $(5, 4)$. All the first members of each pair come from one set and all the second members come from a different set.

This idea can probably best be illustrated if you think of three couples going to a night club for the evening. Pic-

ture all the different ways they could dance together—
Ann with Bill, Ann with John, Kathy with John, etc. If we
follow custom and name ladies first, then you always
know the first member of each pair is the woman, even
with such hard-to-sex names as Meredith and Lindsay.

Listing all the different ways they could be partners we
would have:

| Ann, Bill | Ann, John | Ann, Lindsay |
|-----------|-----------|--------------|
| Kathy, Bill | Kathy, John | Kathy, Lindsay |
| Meredith, Bill | Meredith, John | Meredith, Lindsay |

Only the order would tell a stranger reading the list
which one has on the high heels in the last pair.

Arranged in sets they would be:

$$\text{Set } A = \{\text{Ann, Kathy, Meredith}\}$$
$$\text{Set } B = \{\text{Bill, John, Lindsay}\}$$

Then the Cartesian product of the two sets, written
$A \times B$ and read: "*A* cross *B*," is the list of nine pairs given
above.

Turning this same thing into an algebra problem:

$$\text{Set } A = \{a,b,c\}$$
$$\text{Set } B = \{d,e,f\}$$

$$A \times B = \{(a,d), (a,e), (a,f), (b,d), (b,e), (b,f),$$
$$(c,d), (c,e), (c,f)\}$$

(Notice the members of the first set are always named
first.)

The number of pairs in the new set is nine, the product
of the number of members in *A* times the number in *B*.

A picture of the set of pairs can be made like this:

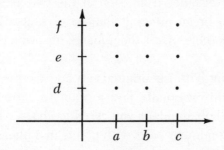

(The mathematical convention is to always name the first set along the horizontal line, the second along the vertical.)

These nine dots are the graph of $A \times B$. Selecting a dot is the same as selecting one of the pairs. For instance, the bottom dot on the right represents the pair $(c,d)$. The dots are in one-to-one correspondence with the members of the set $A \times B$—one dot for each pair, one pair for each dot.

If you do the same thing with numbers, such as $A = \{1,2,3\}$ and $B = \{1,2,3\}$, you will see where the name Cartesian came from. The picture, or graph, looks like this:

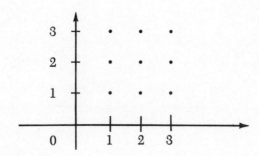

The dots are called lattice points, technically defined as points whose distance from each of the two axes (lines) is either zero or an integral number of units. They are merely the corners of all the squares on ordinary graph paper.

By enlarging both the original sets and the piece of paper, you could eventually find a point to correspond to any pair of whole numbers you cared to choose. This idea of associating number pairs with points in a plane is credited to René Descartes, a French mathematician of the seventeenth century, hence the name Cartesian. It is now tied in with set theory, as so many mathematical concepts are.

### PROBLEMS

1. Write $A \times B$, if $A = \{2,4,6\}$ and $B = \{1,3\}$.

2. Given sets $A = \{1,2,3\}$ and $B = \{5,10,15,20\}$. Write the Cartesian product of $A$ and $B$.

3. Write $S \times S$, where $S = \{1,2,3,4\}$.

# New Arithmetics                                    3

If you read in your child's book that $3 + 4 = 2$, don't be
startled. It does in the modulo five system. Also $4 + 1 = 0$,
$3 + 3 = 1$, and $4 + 4 = 3$. In other words, nothing is sa-
cred any more. However, numbers are used here in a different way.

A modulus is a sort of deuces-wild device that shakes
arithmetic out of its old-time rigidity. It can be any number—a clock works on a modulo twelve system. If it's ten
o'clock now and you add four hours, it is then two, not
fourteen, o'clock. After each circuit of twelve hours, it
starts over. The ordinary sum—14—is reduced by 12,
which is called the modulus.

Nobody intends for this modular, or clock, arithmetic
to replace the ordinary kind. (In fact, it can not.) There
is no movement to introduce it into business. You are not
going to be able to buy a three-dollar steak and a four-
dollar roast and pay the butcher only two dollars. Its purpose is to clarify the structure underlying the fundamental
mathematical operations by working for a while in a different arithmetic, just as when you come home after trav-

eling in a foreign country you see things about your own that you never noticed before. It is a closed-in, limited system, with no fractions, no big numbers, and no negatives. Such a simplified model lets the pupil study addition, subtraction, multiplication, and division without having the point obscured by details.

It is usually introduced in the middle grades—fifth, sixth, or seventh—although there is at present a great deal of overlapping in all this new material. Since, in most cases, students now in high school did not have modular arithmetic when they were in the lower grades, it is put in their textbooks also, with added applications to algebra.

What fools you is that it looks like regular arithmetic. When you see a sentence in French, you know right away that this is not English you are looking at. Even if you don't recognize it as French, you know it is not English.

There is a mathematical symbol—a third bar in the equals sign—that is a warning that the calculation is in a foreign language, so to speak. Technically, the problem should be written $3 + 4 \equiv 2 \pmod 5$ and read: "$3 + 4$ is congruent to 2, modulo 5." However, many books don't use this notation and you just have to find out the hard way, *after* you have told your child that he has added wrong, and then had to eat your words.

MODULO FIVE SYSTEM

Draw a clock face with only five hours on it and you are ready for modulo five arithmetic.

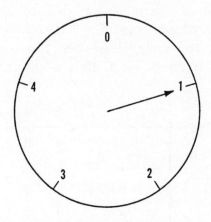

Count to three, then add four more spaces and you are at
2. So $3 + 4 = 2$. You can count the other examples out the
same way. Notice there is no number for five—you are just
back at zero again. Problems in the modulo five system
use only the figures 0,1,2,3,4. You can do any amount
of addition of these numbers by counting around and
around. The answer is never more than four. It can't be—
this system has no higher numbers. If you get tired counting, make yourself an addition table like this:

| + | 0 | 1 | 2 | 3 | 4 |
|---|---|---|---|---|---|
| 0 | 0 | 1 | 2 | 3 | 4 |
| 1 | 1 | 2 | 3 | 4 | 0 |
| 2 | 2 | 3 | 4 | 0 | 1 |
| 3 | 3 | 4 | 0 | 1 | 2 |
| 4 | 4 | 0 | 1 | 2 | 3 |

Multiplication is done the way children and machines do—by repeated additions. $2 \times 3$ means to count two spaces, then two more, then again two more, making three times. It comes out 1. Here is the multiplication table:

| × | 0 | 1 | 2 | 3 | 4 |
|---|---|---|---|---|---|
| 0 | 0 | 0 | 0 | 0 | 0 |
| 1 | 0 | 1 | 2 | 3 | 4 |
| 2 | 0 | 2 | 4 | 1 | 3 |
| 3 | 0 | 3 | 1 | 4 | 2 |
| 4 | 0 | 4 | 3 | 2 | 1 |

Equations are a little more difficult. For instance, in the problem $x + 4 \equiv 2$. You can't transpose—there aren't any negative numbers in a modulo system, since the clock always moves forward. You have to think of a number that would make a zero on the left side of the equation. What added to 4 makes 0? As you see from the addition table, it has to be a 1, so add 1 to both sides:

$$x + 4 + 1 \equiv 2 + 1$$
$$x + 0 \equiv 3$$
$$x \equiv 3$$

Check:
$$3 + 4 \equiv 2$$
$$2 \equiv 2$$

Try a harder problem: $3x + 1 \equiv 3$. First you have to add 4 in order to make a zero:

$$3x + 1 + 4 \equiv 3 + 4$$
$$3x + 0 \equiv 2$$
$$3x \equiv 2$$

Now what to multiply $3x$ by to make $1x$? It takes a 2, so multiply each side:

$$2\ (3x) \equiv 2\ (2)$$
$$1x \equiv 4$$
$$x \equiv 4$$

Check:    $3\ (4)\ +\ 1 \equiv 3$
$$2\ +\ 1 \equiv 3$$
$$3 \equiv 3$$

You probably have figured out by this time that you really don't need a table for the checks at all. Just do the problem in ordinary arithmetic, divide by five, and use only the remainder. It is a little like the method of tallying that everybody knows where the fifth mark goes through the first four: ⫴̸ ‖ . If you disregard the completed bundles and look only at the number of marks in the last group, that is the same as the answer in a modulo five system.

Two numbers are said to be congruent, modulo five, if they have the same remainder when divided by 5. In the check of the problem above, 13 is congruent to 3. Tallied, 13 is ⫴̸ ⫴̸ ‖| ; 3 is ‖| . The unfinished bundles each have three marks in them, therefore the numbers are congruent. So are all numbers that come out that same way—8, ⫴̸ ‖| ; 18, ⫴̸ ⫴̸ ⫴̸ ‖| ; etc. They are also said to belong to the same residue class—residue being what is left over after the groups of five are taken out. 3, 8, 13, and 18 all belong to the 3 class, modulo five. 7 and 12 are in the 2 class, modulo five, because they each have two marks left in the unfinished bundle. That is, they leave a remainder of 2 when divided by 5.

## PROBLEMS

Perform the following computations in the modulo 5 number system:

1. $1 + 2 + 3$
2. $2 + 4 + 2 + 1$
3. $2\,(3)$
4. $3\,(3)(4)$

Solve the following equations in the modulo 5 system:

5. $x + 4 \equiv 0$
6. $3x \equiv 2$
7. $2x + 1 \equiv 3$

8. Find three integers congruent to 4, mod 5.

9. Find three integers that are in the 1 class, mod 5.

10. Find an integer $x$ which satisfies: $x + 3 \equiv 2$, mod 5.

## MODULO TEN SYSTEM

There is nothing special about using five as the modulus—any number will do. A modulo ten system will bring out the similarities to regular arithmetic. Make a clock with ten spaces:

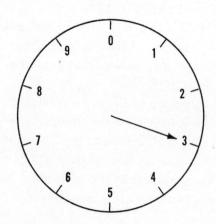

Then $3 + 4 = 7$, $4 + 5 = 9$, and everything looks natural as long as the answer has only one figure. But $6 + 8 = 4$, and $9 + 9 = 8$, because we are dropping off the first figure and writing down only the last one. We are not counting the number of times the hand has gone around—only where it stops. Since that is the case, there is no carrying in modulo ten arithmetic.

By keeping track of the number of times the hand has circled the clock, it is easily converted into ordinary arithmetic. $6 + 8 = 14$, because the hand has gone around once and is now at four. Such an approach helps the child to understand where all the rules about carrying and borrowing come from. The idea is to discover the structure, not memorize a set of rules.

Without this understanding, a child does arithmetic like a color-blind man in a jelly-bean factory trying to sort out the green ones from the red ones. Unable to see the color—the crux of the matter—he has to look for something else to guide him. Maybe the reds are a little blunter at the end, or a trifle smaller. Maybe they smell different. As a last resort he might lick them and separate the peppermint from the wintergreen by taste. In the same way a child looks for something tangible to hang on to, such as: "In division, always invert the second fraction," and memorizes it. This works fine as long as the problems are all alike and there is just one rule, but when the rules pile up to ten or fifteen, that kind of method breaks down. Like the jelly-bean worker, he makes more mistakes and is considerably slower than one who sees the point.

### PROBLEMS

Perform the following computations in the modulo ten system:

1. $6 + 7 + 5$
2. $3(7)$
3. $9 + 5 + 6(3)$

4. Construct an addition table for a modulo seven system.

5. Construct a multiplication table for a modulo three system.

6. Find three integers congruent to 5, mod 7.

Solve the following equations in the modulo ten system:

7. $x + 9 \equiv 1$
8. $7x \equiv 4$

### Modulo Six System

One property of our ordinary arithmetic that is often hazily understood is this: If the product of two numbers is zero, one of them has to be zero. This is not true in every modulo system. Make a clock and a multiplication table using six as a modulus:

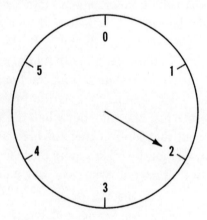

| × | 0 | 1 | 2 | 3 | 4 | 5 |
|---|---|---|---|---|---|---|
| 0 | 0 | 0 | 0 | 0 | 0 | 0 |
| 1 | 0 | 1 | 2 | 3 | 4 | 5 |
| 2 | 0 | 2 | 4 | 0 | 2 | 4 |
| 3 | 0 | 3 | 0 | 3 | 0 | 3 |
| 4 | 0 | 4 | 2 | 0 | 4 | 2 |
| 5 | 0 | 5 | 4 | 3 | 2 | 1 |

From the table you see that 2 times 3 is 0, and so is 4 times 3. You cannot find a single example on a standard multiplication table where two numbers, neither of which is zero, multiply together to equal zero.

Go back and look at the multiplication table for the modulo five system. In every case where the product is zero, one of the factors is zero. It behaves like ordinary arithmetic, in this respect.

Why the difference? Because five is a prime number and six is not. Two times three equals six, and six is replaced by zero in the table. The same is true of four times three because twelve, a multiple of six, is also replaced by zero.

This property (if the product of two numbers is zero, one of them must be zero) is basic in the solution of equations. Since the modulo six system lacks it, equations solved in this system come out strangely. $2x \equiv 4$ has two perfectly good answers: $x \equiv 2$ and $x \equiv 5$. (Ordinarily, an equation has no more solutions than its degree—that is, a first-degree equation, which this is, could have only one.) On the other hand, $2x \equiv 3$ has no solution at all. Look on the table under the column headed 2 and you will see that it is impossible to get a 3, no matter what you multiply by.

Solve the following equations in the modulo six system:

1. $2x \equiv 2$
2. $4x \equiv 2$
3. $4 \equiv 5x$

Perform the following computations in the modulo six system:

4. $5 + 4 + 3$
5. $4 + 4 + 3(5)$
6. Find three integers congruent to 2, modulo six.

## BINARY ARITHMETIC

The simplest modulus you could take is two. Draw a clock with only two spaces on it and two numerals:

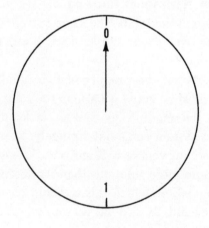

Whatever mathematical computations you perform, the answer is always either 0 or 1. You can't get much more elementary than that.

However, if you try to count the number of times the hand has circled the clock, you will soon run into trouble. How are you going to write that the hand has been around five times when the only symbols at your disposal are 0 and 1? Obviously a whole new system of numeration using two as a base instead of ten has to be constructed. New isn't the right word—such a binary system has been around a long time, but it was regarded as a sort of mathematical curiosity until the advent of the computers.

That pinpoints one of the underlying causes of the mathematics revolution—automation in general and the electronic brains in particular. They do not merely provide a faster way of doing the old math, as you might think, but demand different subject matter.

Since an electric switch has just two choices—on or off —computers represent numbers by using only two symbols, 1 (on) and 0 (off), instead of the 0,1,2,3,4,5,6,7,8,9 that we are used to. In the binary system "110" doesn't mean one hundred and ten—it means six. You do this by changing the invisible headings that we have been schooled to see over each digit.

Instead of:

| Hundreds | Tens | Units |
|----------|------|-------|
| 1 | 1 | 0 |

it becomes:

| Fours | Twos | Units |
|-------|------|-------|
| 1 | 1 | 0 |

In other words, 1 four, 1 two, and no units—they add up
to six. Each heading is twice the one to the right, instead
of ten times it. In this way any number, no matter how
large, can be expressed by just two symbols.

| Sixty-fours | Thirty-twos | Sixteens | Eights | Fours | Twos | Units |
|:---:|:---:|:---:|:---:|:---:|:---:|:---:|
| 1 | 1 | 0 | 1 | 0 | 1 | 1 |

Add them up and you get one hundred and seven. This
may be cumbersome for us, but it's convenient for the
machines, and, brother, that's what counts.

Those who work with computers call the binary digits
"bits." Professor Franklin McFeely, in an article in the
May, 1959, *Mathematics Teacher* called, "One Plus One
Equals Toon," suggests regular names for the numbers
in the binary system. Toon, written 10, is two, three is
etooven (11), four (100) is toodred, etc. These names
have not caught on, but you do need something to call 10
—you have to fight the temptation to say "ten." The best
we can do at present is to read it "one zero," or "one two
and zero."

To understand addition in binary arithmetic, think of
the numbers as rows of light bulbs, each individual bulb
turned on for 1, off for 0. Then picture a row of bulbs for
the answer, each one wired to the ones in the column
above it in such a way that it flashes on or off according
to the sum of the digits in that column.

$$
\begin{array}{r}
1\ 1\ 0 \\
+1\ 0\ 1 \\
\hline
1\ 0\ 1\ 1
\end{array}
\qquad
\text{Check:}
\begin{array}{r}
6 \\
+5 \\
\hline
11
\end{array}
$$

Starting at the right, $1 + 0 = 1$, so that light comes on in
the answer. The same is true in the second column. But in

the third one, $1 + 1$ is more than one. Some other arrangement has to be made. It is handled by having that bulb go off and the one in the column to the left flash on —in other words, a mechanism for carrying one. The problem is checked by converting it to ordinary arithmetic.

The addition table is as follows:

| + | 0 | 1 |
|---|---|---|
| 0 | 0 | 1 |
| 1 | 1 | 10 |

Use it to solve this problem:

```
  1 0 1 1 1        Check:    23
 +1 0 1 0                   +10
 ---------                  ----
1 0 0 0 0 1                  33
```

The multiplication table is easier:

| × | 0 | 1 |
|---|---|---|
| 0 | 0 | 0 |
| 1 | 0 | 1 |

Multiplying by a single digit is child's play—the answer is always either identical with the first number, or it is zero.

```
  1 0 1 1 0        Check:    22
 ×       1                 ×  1
 ---------                  ----
  1 0 1 1 0                  22
```

```
  1 0 1 1 0        Check:    22
 ×       0                 ×  0
 ---------                  ----
  0 0 0 0 0                   0
```

When a two-digit multiplier is used, the problem is harder, since addition is involved.

```
  1 0 1 1 0              Check:      22
×       1 1                        ×  3
  ─────────                        ────
  1 0 1 1 0                          66
1 0 1 1 0
─────────────
1 0 0 0 0 1 0
```

Although the binary system has a practical application in computer mathematics, this is only a secondary reason for introducing it into the school curriculum. The primary purpose is to give insight into the workings and structure of ordinary, base ten, arithmetic. The decimal system is so familiar that the reasons underlying its operations are often overlooked, but handling a strange system affords an opportunity for the discovery of these reasons, which are common to all number systems.

In most programs, the binary system is taught in grade six or seven, but since many of the students now in high school did not have it at that level, it is also included in some of their textbooks (for example, *Advanced High School Mathematics* by Vannatta, Carnahan, and Fawcett) with harder applications.

### PROBLEMS

Change each of the following binary numerals to their equivalent in the ordinary, base ten, system:

1. 1100
2. 1010
3. 111
4. 110011
5. 1111100

Assuming that the following are numerals in the base two system, perform the indicated computations in binary arithmetic:

6.  111 + 101
7.  1101 + 1111
8.  1011 × 10
9.  111001 × 111
10. 110 (11011 + 1011)

## OTHER BASES

For convenience in working with computers, bits are often divided into groups of three. In that case the headings are fours, twos, and units, repeated over and over. Since four + two + one is seven, each trio of bits can express any number from 0 through 7:

| fours | twos | units | fours | twos | units | fours | twos | units |
|:-----:|:----:|:-----:|:-----:|:----:|:-----:|:-----:|:----:|:-----:|
| 1 | 1 | 0 | 0 | 1 | 1 | 1 | 0 | 1 |
| | 6 | | | 3 | | | 5 | |

But this is not six hundred and thirty-five. We are now using eight symbols—0,1,2,3,4,5,6,7—which means that we are in a number system with a base of eight, the octal system. Its headings are:

| Sixty-fours | Eights | Units |
|:-----------:|:------:|:-----:|
| 6 | 3 | 5 |

Worked out: $6(64) + 3(8) + 5(1)$ equals 413 in the ordinary, or base ten, system.

Some computers work in base eight, but you do not have to confine your study of number systems to those that have practical applications. Once you get used to this free-wheeling idea, you can make up a number system using any base you want to. Base five is probably the easiest and, therefore, is taught first. The School Mathematics Study Group texts present it in the fifth grade; the Greater Cleveland Mathematics Program proposes it for the fourth.

The Babylonians used a base of sixty, the Mayas of Yucatán calculated in base twenty. The Duodecimal Society of America has, for a number of years, been trying to get the United States to change over to a base of twelve, on the grounds that twelve makes computation easier since it is divisible by two, three, four, and six, and that it is more compatible with many of our common measures— twelve things in a dozen, twelve inches in a foot, three feet in a yard, etc.

The only reason most civilizations have used ten is that humans happen to have ten fingers. If it should turn out that the Martians have sixteen, then the astronauts will probably find them using a system based on sixteen.

If you would like to compute in such a pseudo-Martian system, you need sixteen number symbols. Since we have only ten, you will have to piece out with letters: 0,1,2,3,4, 5,6,7,8,9,a,b,c,d,e,f,   where   a = ten,   b = eleven,   c = twelve,   d = thirteen,   e = fourteen,   f = fifteen. Here is an addition problem:

| Sixteen sixteens (Two hundred fifty-six) | Sixteens | Units | |
|---|---|---|---|
| 1 | 5 | b | (This is 347, earth style) |
| 3 | c | 8 | (968) |
| 5 | 2 | 3 | (1315) |

It is done exactly the same way as in the decimal system.
Beginning on the right:

Units

b   (i.e., 11')
8
___
19

Take sixteen units out, roll them together into 1 sixteen,
and carry it to the next column, leaving 3 units

Sixteens

1  (carried)
5
c  (i.e., 12)
___
18

Take sixteen of these sixteens out, bundle them up into
1 two-hundred fifty-six, and carry it to the next column,
leaving 2 of them behind.

Two hundred fifty-six

1  (carried)
1
3
___
5

You can see the necessity for indicating which base is
being used. Otherwise there would be a mathematical
Tower of Babel, with everybody calculating in a different
system. It is customary to write the base as a subscript to
the right of the last figure—$635_{eight}$, $413_{ten}$, or $110011101_{two}$.
(These are all really the same number—work them out
and see.) There is a technical reason for writing the sub-
scripts in words instead of numerals. The octal system has

no symbol for eight, therefore it would not be correct to write $635_8$. The same is true for every system—there is no symbol 2 in the binary system, no symbol 5 in the quinary system, no 16 in the base sixteen system. Many textbooks, as a practical matter of convenience, however, do write $635_8$ and all the other bases in a similar way. It's a sort of gentlemen's agreement, to save time, although the gentlemen all know it is not technically accurate to do so.

You also need some way of changing numbers from one system to another. The method of converting from a different base into base ten has already been indicated above —just multiply each digit by the heading of its column and add all the results. To go the other way—from base ten to a new system—there is a handy algorithm that does the trick. ("Algorithm" is an old-fashioned word, meaning a step-by-step procedure, which has come back into style because computers require step-by-step procedures.) This is the remainder method. Start with the number in base ten and divide over and over by the new base, writing down the remainders each time. Then list the remainders *in reverse order* and there is the number in the new base. For example, to convert $23_{ten}$ to the binary system:

$$2\,\overline{)\,23}$$
$$2\,\overline{)\,11} \text{ Remainder } 1$$
$$2\,\overline{)\,\phantom{0}5} \text{ Remainder } 1$$
$$2\,\overline{)\,\phantom{0}2} \text{ Remainder } 1$$
$$2\,\overline{)\,\phantom{0}1} \text{ Remainder } 0$$
$$\phantom{2)}\,0 \text{ Remainder } 1$$

$10111_{two} = 23_{ten}$

That same number—$23_{ten}$—changed to base five would be:

$$5)\underline{23}$$
$$5)\underline{\phantom{0}4} \text{ Remainder 3}$$
$$0 \text{ Remainder 4}$$

$43_{five} = 23_{ten}$

Notice that the smaller the base, the longer the number turns out to be, which is logical, since you have fewer symbols at your disposal and have to repeat them over and over to express any given number.

It is difficult to change directly from one of these exotic systems to another without going through base ten first, since the calculating would have to be done in one of the strange systems. If you want to change $32_{five}$ to base seven, it is easier to first convert to the equivalent in base ten, and then go to base seven, doing all the computing in the good old decimal system.

The exception (among the systems we have discussed) is in changing back and forth between the binary and the octal system. Since the cube of 2 (the base of one system) equals 8 (the base of the other), the numerals can be converted directly by grouping, as explained at the beginning of this section.

PROBLEMS

Change each of the following to equivalent decimal numerals:

1. $125_{eight}$
2. $29_{sixteen}$
3. $312_{five}$
4. $910_{twelve}$

Change each of the following decimal numerals to the indicated base:

5. 93 to base five
6. 45 to base two
7. 173 to base twelve
8. 105 to base two
9. Change $110010101_{two}$ to the octal numeration system.
10. Change $213_{five}$ to the binary numeration system.

Within the lifetime of children now in grade school space ships *may* be going to Mars, but even if there *are* inhabitants there and even if they *should* have sixteen of whatever it is they have (antennae, maybe?) that is not the purpose of teaching this new arithmetic. To sum up, most programs advance the following reasons for adding it to the curriculum:

1. It gives a better understanding of the structure of the conventional decimal, base ten, number system.
2. It has a practical application to computers.
3. Converting from one system to another provides an opportunity for interesting drill in ordinary addition, subtraction, multiplication, and division.

# Number Systems

The School Mathematics Study Group's textbook for the sixth grade has a problem about a bug named Willie who crawled along a number line. This is typical of the widespread use of the number line as a teaching device all the way from the first grade through high school. It is simply a horizontal line marked off into equal intervals with the numbers named in order from left to right, smaller to larger. Such a concrete geometrical picture makes certain facts about the numbers very vivid. For instance, you can plainly see that $-3$ is smaller than $-2$ because the point for $-3$ is to the left of the point for $-2$, and that $\frac{1}{5}$ is larger than $\frac{3}{16}$ because the point for $\frac{1}{5}$ is to the right of the point for $\frac{3}{16}$.

The fact that numbers can be associated with points in order along a straight line seems so obvious that it doesn't need any comment, but in the formal study of number systems, order is one of the first properties to be examined. It means that of two numbers, $a$ and $b$, $a$ is always either greater than $b$, equal to $b$, or smaller than $b$. There are number systems that lack this property, as you will see later.

If Willie is a very perceptive bug he can get a good idea of what grade he is in by noticing the kinds of numbers that are printed along the line. If they are all what are called natural numbers, he is in one of the primary grades. If fractions are included, then it is the fourth, fifth, or sixth. When negative and irrational numbers are added, he is probably in junior high school. If there are two number lines drawn perpendicular to each other, which are necessary to illustrate complex numbers, then Willie has reached the latter part of high school.

All these different kinds of numbers are not the result of any one person's conscious effort, but evolved slowly and painfully over a long period of time. They are the end product of several thousand years of human thought. The order in which they are put in the school curriculum roughly parallels the historical order in which they were developed.

### NATURAL NUMBERS

What are natural numbers? Those a child uses when he learns to count. I never heard one say: "1, 1½, —2, $\sqrt{3}$." They are always signless whole numbers. Savages count the same way. How high they go depends on the state of advancement of their civilization. A few primitive tribes have no word for a number beyond 3—they just say "many."

The early Greeks had names for numbers only up to a myriad (ten thousand). Then, in the third century B.C., Archimedes wrote a treatise called "The Sand Reckoner" describing a new system for generating and expressing very large numbers—large enough to count not only all the grains of sand in the whole earth, even if the seas and valleys were filled up level with the mountaintops, but all the sand in the universe, which he pictured as a sphere with a radius reaching to the stars, if it were filled up the same way. His estimate of the size of this sphere was considerably off, extending only a little beyond where we now know the planet Saturn to be, but it was huge enough to serve his purpose—namely, to show that even these gigantic quantities could be counted.

First he figured how many grains of sand placed side by side would equal the diameter of a poppy seed, then how many poppy seeds would equal a finger's breadth, and so on up. Starting from a myriad, he invented new numbers to count all this sand, arranging them into orders and periods. His first order ended with a myriad myriad, or one hundred million, which he called an octade. This then became the unit for the second order, which went up to an octade octades. The third order, in turn, climbed to an octade octade octades, etc. The orders were grouped into periods of increasingly enormous size—the first period ended with a number we would write as 1 followed by eight hundred million zeros, which, in turn, became the unit for the first order of the second period. This method could turn out numbers indefinitely. Archimedes developed it up to a number that we would have to express as 1 followed by eighty thousand million million zeros, which he demonstrated was more than adequate for counting the grains of all that hypothetical sand.

In modern mathematices we would count them in googols. If the word sounds as if it were made up by a child, it is because it was. Dr. Edward Kasner's nine-year-old nephew thought up the name, on request. Written out, it is:

10,000,000,000,000,000,000,000,000,000,000,000,
000,000,000,000,000,000,000,000,000,000,000,000,
000,000,000,000,000,000,000,000,000.

More compactly, it is expressed as $10^{100}$. In this abbreviated notation the exponent tells you how many zeros you would have to put after the 1 if it were written the long way.

A googol is just about large enough to accommodate the largest numbers used in physics or astronomy. When the need arises for larger ones, mathematicians are ready with the googolplex (named by the same child). This is 1 followed by a googol of zeros. I couldn't write it out on this page, or in this entire book, nor on all the pages of all the books ever written. There wouldn't be room for all those zeros. In scientific notation it is $10^{10^{100}}$, which means to raise ten to the googolth power.

But no matter how big, these are all just plain numbers, derived from counting—brothers and sisters of the ones on the number line in the first grade.

There, using numbers of much more modest size, a number line is used for teaching addition. If the problem is $2 + 3$, start at the left and count two spaces, then three more. There you are at five, the answer.

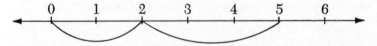

Whether zero should be written on the line for little children is debatable. It is not a natural number—even the

Greeks didn't have it—and was not formerly taught at this grade level. However, Patrick Suppes, in his book *Sets and Numbers*, explains zero to the children as the number of members of the empty set, illustrated by { }. He says that experimental work has shown that first-graders have no special difficulty with this concept, and that zero is as easy for them as any other number, when introduced in this way.

For subtraction, start at the right and work toward the left. To do $6 - 2$, start at 6, then count to the left two spaces and there is the answer at four.

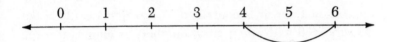

Multiplication, say $2 \times 3$, means to take two steps, each three spaces long, going from left to right.

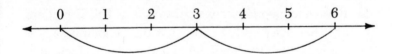

To illustrate $7 \div 2$, start at 7 and work toward the left, taking steps two spaces long until there isn't room for any more. The spaces left over are the remainder; the number of steps you took is the answer.

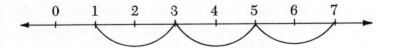

PROBLEMS

1. Which is larger, an octade or a googol?

2. Which is larger, a googol or the largest number developed by Archimedes?

3. Which is larger, a googolplex or the largest number developed by Archimedes?

4. Into which one of Archimedes' orders of the first period would a googol fit?

RATIONAL NUMBERS

In the practical business of measuring, which consists of applying an arbitrary unit to an object and counting the number of times it is contained, the ancients could make do very well with the natural numbers as long as it came out even, but when it didn't—and it usually didn't—they were forced to employ fractions, a major step in the mathematics of antiquity.

At first they were handled very awkwardly. The Babylonians used only fractions whose denominator was 60; the Roman denominator was always 12. The Egyptians, on the other hand, didn't care what the denominator was, but insisted that the numerator had to be 1. Instead of $\frac{3}{4}$ they wrote the sum of $\frac{1}{2}$ and $\frac{1}{4}$. (The only exception they tolerated was $\frac{2}{3}$.) The Rhind papyrus, a sort of mathematical handbook called "Directions for Knowing All Dark Things," which was written by the Egyptian priest, Ahmes, seventeen hundred years before Christ, devotes a lot of space to a table showing division converted to this form. It wasn't easy—for instance, $2 \div 29$ had to be written as the sum of $\frac{1}{24}$, $\frac{1}{58}$, $\frac{1}{174}$, and $\frac{1}{232}$ instead of $\frac{2}{29}$, as we do.

In the Encyclopaedia Britannica Films, Inc. textbooks for the elementary grades, called *Math Workshop for Children*, problems on this historical mathematics are included. For example, you might be asked to write a fraction like ⅝ as the sum of three unit fractions, in the Egyptian fashion: ¼ + ¼ + ⅛ would work.* So would ½ + ⅟₁₆ + ⅟₁₆. The object is to bring home to the student the advantages of our method by having him experience a little of the inconvenience and clumsiness of operating in another way.

It took centuries before the fractional numbers were accepted on an equal footing with the other numbers. For one thing, they don't have the same concrete character. The natural numbers stand like a row of columns, but if you try to fill the spaces between them with a picket fence of fractions you run into trouble, because a fractional number has no successor. If I ask what is the next whole number after 2, you say 3, but what's the next fractional number after ½? What do you paint on that picket? There's no way to tell—the possibilities are infinite. Mathematicians call this property "density" and define it by saying that between any pair of fractional numbers another one can always be inserted, endlessly. It is hard to get a thought picture of a fence of fractions if you are always moving the pickets over and crowding in another one, closer and closer.

To be exact, what the mathematicians say is that between any two *rational* numbers another one can always be inserted, rational being the name given to the kinds of

---

* The Egyptians did not use repetitions of the same fraction, but children in grade-school are often allowed to.

numbers we have mentioned so far because they can all be written as ratios: 2/3, or 64/25, or 3/1. If you try to draw a number line of the rational numbers, you are faced with a problem. Since there are infinitely many fractions between any two whole numbers, which ones are you going to put on the line? All you can do is write in a few as examples.

In the painful transition from the natural number system to the rational number system (i.e., he now has to cope with fractions in his problems), which the child makes at about the fourth grade, things will be easier if he can be led to see that all that has been changed is the unit of measurement. Mark a number line off all the way across in ⅓'s. Then, if you disregard the denominators, you can add and subtract in exactly the same way as with whole numbers.

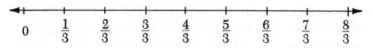

$$0 \qquad \frac{1}{3} \qquad \frac{2}{3} \qquad \frac{3}{3} \qquad \frac{4}{3} \qquad \frac{5}{3} \qquad \frac{6}{3} \qquad \frac{7}{3} \qquad \frac{8}{3}$$

Even that old bugaboo, the common denominator, can be explained on the number line. Say you want to find the lowest common denominator for ½, ⅓, and ¼. Count by twos, by threes, and by fours, until they all meet for the first time and that's it—12.

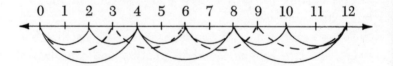

Since decimal fractions look and act much more like the numerals for whole numbers than do common fractions, there are some who advocate teaching decimals first. Such an idea was presented at the SMSG conference on elementary school mathematics held in Chicago in 1959. However, most courses of study continue to start with the common fractions.

1. Write each of the following fractions in the Egyptian way, the Babylonian way, and the Roman way: $\frac{5}{6}$; $\frac{3}{4}$; $\frac{5}{10}$; $\frac{5}{15}$; $\frac{2}{3}$.

2. Find the least common denominator of $\frac{1}{8}$, $\frac{2}{3}$, and $\frac{3}{4}$ by means of a number line.

3. Insert a rational number between $\frac{5}{16}$ and $\frac{7}{9}$. Now insert another rational number between that one and $\frac{5}{16}$.

## IRRATIONAL NUMBERS

While it is true that there is a point on the number line for every rational number, the opposite does not hold—there is not a rational number for every point. In the preceding section, the number lines had only a few fractions put in as examples. You *could* fill in millions until the line was black with them, but even so, dense as the fractions may be, there are gaps in that line where no number in the rational system will fit. That is because there are things—the diagonals of some squares, for instance—that no rational number can measure exactly.

Construct a square with one unit as its side and draw the diagonal, then put the point of a compass on $A$ and cut an arc. The distance along the line from $A$ to $P$ is the same length as the diagonal.

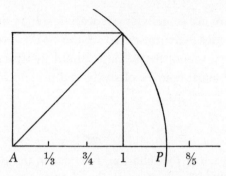

$A$    $\frac{1}{3}$   $\frac{3}{4}$   $1$   $P$   $\frac{8}{5}$

$P$ may appear to fall on one of the rational numbers, but that is just because a construction can't be perfect—the width of the pencil mark covers a little space, while a point, technically, has no thickness. Actually, $P$ is a point without a rational number. It cannot hit on one of the rationals because the length of the diagonal is irrational, a fact the Greeks discovered very early.

It was the Pythagoreans, a mystic brotherhood devoted to the study of mathematics and astronomy, who found this out when they were pursuing their famous theorem that the square on the hypotenuse of a right triangle is equivalent to the sum of the squares on the other two sides. You can see how it happened if you take the square you constructed and, since the diagonal divides it into two right triangles, apply their theorem as follows:

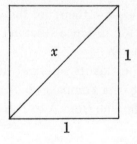

$$x^2 = 1^2 + 1^2$$
$$x^2 = 2$$
$$x = \sqrt{2}$$

But there is no rational number which multiplied by itself equals 2. If you look it up on a square-root table today and find 1.414, that is only an approximation, rounded off at the third decimal place. Square it and you get 1.999396, not 2. If you use a larger table you find $\sqrt{2}$ is 1.4142136, also an approximation. Give the problem to a computer and it will work until it wears itself out, if you don't turn it off. There is no number that is the square root of 2—no rational number, that is. Therefore it must be, by definition, irrational.

If you start the other way and call the diagonal 1, then the side comes out $\frac{1}{2}\sqrt{2}$, which is just as bad. There is simply something about that square which eludes the rational number system.

This discovery spread consternation among the Pythagoreans. Not only were they forced to scrap some of their mathematical theories, but it also struck at the heart of their philosophy. In their search for the world-stuff out of which everything else is created, they had come to hold the strange belief that "all things are numbers." Mixing a great deal of what we would call numerology with their mathematics, they had made a sort of religion out of the whole numbers. Yet here was a line that could be measured neither by a whole number nor a ratio of whole numbers.

The Greeks wrestled with the problem for years. They produced an airtight theoretical proof that $\sqrt{2}$ could not be rational. Theodorus of Cyrene, a Pythagorean who is said to have been Plato's teacher, discovered many more irrationals: $\sqrt{3}$, $\sqrt{5}$, $\sqrt{6}$, $\sqrt{7}$, $\sqrt{8}$, $\sqrt{10}$, $\sqrt{11}$, $\sqrt{12}$, $\sqrt{13}$, $\sqrt{14}$, $\sqrt{15}$, and $\sqrt{17}$.

Since the Greek numerals were merely the letters of their alphabet with no place value attached—α was one, β was two, etc.—they could not use decimal approximations, as we do. To try to evaluate such intractable numbers they hit upon the ingenious method of "the great and the small" which closed in on the irrationals from above and below.

First they constructed a ladder of numbers like this:

$$
\begin{array}{cc}
1 & 1 \\
2 & 3 \\
5 & 7 \\
12 & 17 \\
29 & 41 \\
\text{etc.} &
\end{array}
$$

The ratio of the two numbers on each rung comes nearer and nearer to the ratio $1/\sqrt{2}$. 2/3 is a little too small; 5/7 is a bit too large; 12/17 is again too small, but closer than 2/3. As you go along the rungs of the ladder, the elusive ratio is caught in a sort of pincer movement.

The irrationals achieved status as bona-fide numbers when Plato, who was much influenced by the Pythagoreans, included them on an equal footing with the rationals in his lectures at the Academy. One of his pupils, the brilliant Eudoxus, put the theory of irrationals on such a sound logical basis that this masterpiece of ancient arithmetic was not equaled until the nineteenth century.

Students today meet irrationals in junior high school, usually when they get to elementary algebra, although some programs present it earlier. There are several ways of treating irrational numbers, all developed within the last century, which qualifies them as new math. The former curriculum included nothing more recent than seventeenth-century developments. The twenty-fourth yearbook of the National Council of Teachers of Mathematics presents irrationals as nested intervals; the *Appendices to the Report of the Commission on Mathematics* of the College Entrance Examination Board recommends the non-repeating decimal approach. Some textbooks follow one, some the other.

The number-within-a-nest method is similar to the Greek idea of squeezing the irrational from both sides, but expressed in our decimal notation and illustrated on a number line. You begin by thinking of the two nearest perfect squares. If the problem is to find the square root of 2, you see that it falls between $\sqrt{1}$, which is 1, and $\sqrt{4}$, which is 2. The first interval is that part of the number line between 1 and 2. Divide that into ten equal spaces. By squaring the endpoints of the most likely of those intervals, you find that $\sqrt{2}$ falls between 1.4 and 1.5 because 2 falls between the square of 1.4 and the square of 1.5. Divide *that* interval into ten parts, try those, and you see that it is between 1.41 and 1.42. As you keep this up, the size of the innermost of the nest of intervals keeps shrinking until, theoretically, every other number is eventually shut out, leaving $\sqrt{2}$ and nothing else.

The approach of the Commission on Mathematics is to consider all numbers as unending decimals. Your are familiar with .333. . . for ⅓. (This is usually written with a line over the 3 to show it repeats: $.\overline{3}$). In the same way ⅔ is $.\overline{6}$ and ⅐ is $.\overline{142857}$, repeated over and over. By fudging a little and adding zeros, those that come out even, such as $\frac{1}{2} = .5$, can be represented as repeating: $\frac{1}{2} = .5\overline{0}$. These are all rational numbers. When the irrationals are expressed as unending decimals, the difference is that they never repeat. Maybe one or two figures do, here and there, but there is no repetitive sequence, as in $\frac{1}{7} = .\overline{142857}$. $\sqrt{2}$ is $1.4142136\ldots$, continued indefinitely, always different.

In such a way the irrational numbers were fitted into the domain of mathematics.

## PROBLEMS

1. Discover the rule for selecting the numbers used on the Greeks' ladder and extend it three more rungs.

2. Convert each rung to a decimal fraction. Compare them with the decimal value of $1/\sqrt{2}$. (For ease in computation this is the same as $\frac{1}{2}\sqrt{2}$.)

3. Extend the nest of intervals for the square root of 2 to the next three smaller. Compare their intervals with the decimal approximation of $\sqrt{2}$, given above.

## NEGATIVE NUMBERS

Negative numbers, though simpler to understand, were not invented until long after the irrationals. Natural numbers are used when things are counted, fractions when things are measured, and irrational numbers are necessary for geometrical figures, but negative numbers do not occur naturally in relation to concrete objects. They are brought about by a property of number systems called closure. We say the natural numbers are closed under addition, which means that, if you add any two natural numbers, the answer is always a natural number. But this is true of subtraction only if you subtract the small number from the large one. If the natural numbers are the only ones at your disposal, a problem such as $3 - 5$ is impossible, meaning it is impossible in that number system. Extending the system to include fractions and irrationals does not help in subtracting 5 from 3. The system, as we have developed it so far, is not closed under subtraction.

The ancients did not solve this problem. Diophantus, one of the last of the Greeks, spoke of the "impossible solution of the absurd equation $4x + 16 = 4$"—a dead giveaway that he didn't have any negative numbers and therefore could not subtract 16 from 4. Today any first-year algebra student can find that $x = -3$.

The Greeks died, their great university at Alexandria fell to the Moors, and nothing of any great moment happened in Western mathematics for around a thousand years. The history of the subject passed to Arabia and India. There some unnamed genius invented the positional notation system—the way of writing numbers in Hindu-Arabic numerals that we are used to, including zero as a placeholder. (How could you tell 23 from 203 without a zero?) The idea of a number symbol, 0, for none was new to mankind. It is an unnatural number, calling for a certain amount of mathematical sophistication in order to understand all its properties—more sophistication than the ancient civilizations had, in fact.

Zero made it possible to subtract a number from its equal and have something to write for an answer. The next step was to find a way to take a large number from a smaller one—that way was the use of negatives. By the twelfth century, Bhaskara, a Hindu mathematician, wrote of solving a quadratic equation which came out $x = 50$ and $x = -5$. However, he remarked, "The second root is not to be taken, for it is inadequate. People do not approve of negative roots." They were still not psychologically ready for such an elastic concept of number.

The Hindu-Arabic notation and algebra were introduced into medieval Italy by Leonardo of Pisa (also called Fibonacci), who based his work on an Arabic treatise. He made one of the earliest attempts to give a concrete meaning to negative numbers by saying that in problems concerning profit, a negative answer meant a loss. This points up the basic idea necessary in extending the number line to include negatives—that of direction.

Algebra spread northward with the Renaissance. European mathematicians, like those in India, were dubious about negative numbers, using them when necessary but always with suspicion. They were not generally accepted until the seventeenth century. Even later, some diehards held out against the "strange doctrine of negative quantities," saying it was ruining the "otherwise clear and simple science of algebra."

When all these kinds of numbers are put together they make up the real number system. Shown on a number line it looks this way:

$$-3 \quad -\sqrt{7} \quad -2 \quad -\tfrac{3}{2} \quad -1 \quad -\tfrac{1}{3} \quad 0 \quad \tfrac{1}{2} \quad 1 \quad \sqrt{2} \quad \tfrac{5}{3} \quad 2 \quad 1\tfrac{2}{5} \quad 3$$

Zero is in the middle, the positive numbers to the right and the negatives to the left, running off in both directions as far as you like. Instead of a series of isolated points, it is continuous. There are no gaps. There is a number for every possible point and a point for every possible real number—a one-to-one correspondence between the real number system and the points on the number line. To reach this happy state of affairs had taken several thousand years of human thought.

### PROBLEMS

$$6, \tfrac{3}{4}, \sqrt{5}, 0, -12, 6\tfrac{1}{4}, \sqrt{16}, \sqrt{\tfrac{1}{4}}, -5\tfrac{1}{2}, -\sqrt{10}, (\tfrac{1}{2}+\tfrac{1}{4}),$$
$$(\tfrac{1}{4}-\tfrac{1}{2}), 5 -\sqrt{3}, 1.32\overline{156}$$

1. Which of the numbers in the list above are natural numbers?

2. Which are rational numbers but not natural numbers?

3. Which are both rational and natural?

4. Which are real but not rational?

5. Which are real and rational but not natural?

## COMPLEX NUMBERS

You think now with natural numbers, fractions, negatives, zero, and irrationals we are all set for any eventuality? Then suppose you try to solve the equation $x^2 = -9$. Now what? According to the law of signs, $(3)^2 = 9$ and $(-3)^2 = 9$, also. What squared makes $-9$? If you try to weasel out of it by saying 3 times $-3$, that's not squaring—the number has to be multiplied by *itself*. Here we go again. There isn't any real number whose square is negative, so obviously some unreal ones had to be invented, and they were—the imaginaries. Instead of being made of solid building blocks of 1's, they are constructed of units of $i$'s (for imaginary), and connected to the real numbers by the arbitrary definition that $i^2 = -1$.

One answer to the problem above is $3i$. (Separate $-9$ into 9 times $-1$, then replace $-1$ by $i^2$. If $x = 3i$, then $x^2 = 9i^2$.)

If negative numbers were hard for people to swallow, imaginaries were ten times as bad. The Brahmin Bhaskara, in the twelfth century, outlawed answers such as $x = \sqrt{-9}$ by writing. "The square of a positive number, as also that of a negative number, is positive. There is no square root of a negative number, for a negative number is not a square." In the sixteenth century the Italian mathematician, Cardan, went so far as to write down $(5 + \sqrt{-15})\,(5 - \sqrt{-15})$ as the solution to a problem, but he made the reservation that it was meaningless, fictitious, and imaginary.

Such mathematical expressions kept occurring, to the point where they become as unavoidable as fractions and negatives. To achieve freedom in computation, the imaginary numbers had to be used and for the same reason the fractions and decimals were—closure. The real number system is not closed under the operations performed in solving quadratic and cubic equations.

The name imaginary stuck, which is unfortunate, implying as it does something out of fairyland, supernatural and hallucinatory. They have many very real applications, especially in problems concerning alternating current electricity.

It is quite possible to start with concrete data, perform many and complicated mathematical manipulations, running into imaginary numbers along the way, and have the whole thing turn back into real numbers in the end. This is because of the following basic pattern:

$$i = \sqrt{-1}$$
$$i^2 = -1$$
$$i^3 = -1(i) \text{ or } -i$$
$$i^4 = -1(-1) \text{ or } 1$$

At alternate steps, beginning with the second, you are back in the real number system.

The hybrid form, such as $2 + 3i$, in which the roots of quadratic equations often appear is called a complex number—part real, part imaginary. The general form is $a + bi$. If $b = 0$, then the whole expression is merely a real number. If $a = 0$, then the number is a pure imaginary. Therefore all real numbers (including naturals, rationals, zero, negatives, and irrationals) as well as imaginaries are encompassed in the complex number system.

It takes a plane with *two* number lines to show all these kinds of numbers. The second one, for the imaginaries, is drawn perpendicular to the other. The two lines determine the complex plane on which any complex number can be represented by a point, as you see in the Argand diagram below (named for Monsieur Argand, a Parisian bookkeeper who was one of three people to invent it at about the same time—i.e., the nineteenth century).

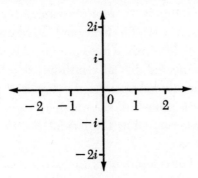

In the new mathematics a complex number is treated as an ordered pair of real numbers $(a, b)$. (See chapter on sets, section on Cartesian product.) This viewpoint is summarized in the *Principles of Mathematics* by Allendoerfer and Oakley: "For historical reasons, $a$ is called the real part of $a + bi$ and $b$ is called its imaginary part. No significance is attached to these words; they are mere labels denoting 'first' and 'second' member of the pair $(a, b)$."

### Problems

1. Which of the following are actually real numbers in disguise? $i$, $i^2$, $3i^3$, $i^6$, $-i^4$, $2i^8$, $-5i$

2. Treating $i$ as any letter in algebra, multiply $2 + 3i$ by $2 - 3i$. Is your answer a real or imaginary number?

The school curriculum now includes a systematic study of the number system because of a general trend on the part of mathematicians to tidy up and streamline what is, historically, a rather jerry-built edifice. It has been nailed together over the centuries as the need arose, with here a suite for the integers, there a mezzanine for the fractions, and yonder an attic for irrational numbers. Part of the architecture is Moorish. There are cupolas and spires and minarets, connected by labyrinthine corridors and stairways and elevator shafts. At the top is a mooring mast tethering a dirigible full of imaginary numbers—units of $i$'s that are as ethereal as the gas-filled cells that kept the zeppelins afloat.

The logical development of the various number systems,

as shown by the following chart, is slightly different from the historical order.

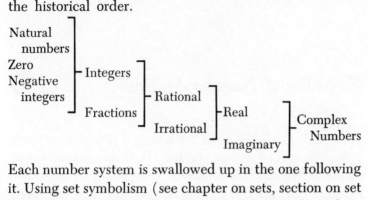

Each number system is swallowed up in the one following it. Using set symbolism (see chapter on sets, section on set inclusion), the relationship between the sets of numbers would be:

Natural numbers ⊂ Integers ⊂ Rational ⊂ Real ⊂ Complex Numbers

You might think that this process of extension would have to go on indefinitely, but that is not the case. Start with complex numbers, perform any algebraic operations you want to with them, and, praises be, the answer is always another complex number. In other words, the set of complex numbers is closed under all algebraic operations, except for dividing by 0 and $0^0$.

We had to give up something to achieve this though—the property of order. Since the complex numbers correspond to points scattered over a plane, instead of being marshaled along a straight line like the reals, it is impossible to say whether $3 + 4i$ is greater than, equal to, or smaller than $4 + 3i$.

# *Properties of Number Systems* 5

Pick up your child's math book and, if it is new enough, you will see references to the ACD laws—association, commutation, and distribution. The principles contained in these laws are already familiar to you. You use them, without realizing it, whenever you add, subtract, multiply, or divide. In fact, stating them in this formal fashion is roughly equivalent to a man's buying a marriage license and going through a ceremony with his common-law wife after twenty years and ten children together. Two plus three equals three plus two and has for quite some time, but five thousand years and billions of bastard answers later we have the law of commutation which says, "The sum of two numbers is not affected by the order in which they are added," and legitimizes the whole thing.

They are in the textbooks because of the current emphasis on deductive proof. Since mathematics is man-made, it is not infallible. There have been times in the past when cracks have appeared in the structure—notably the Pythagoreans' discovery of the irrationality of $\sqrt{2}$, referred to in Chapter IV—because part of it was based only on what is usually called common sense. Therefore, a rigorous proof is necessary for each new invention. This is part of the trend away from physical reality and toward abstract theory which is a characteristic of modern mathematics.

In the long history of man's attempts at problem solving the pendulum has swung back and forth between empirical and theoretical methods. The empiricists collect a number of examples, tabulate the results, and then make what amounts to an informed guess about the answer to all similar problems. It is never absolutely certain, but only *probably* correct, even if a thousand cases have come out the same way—the thousand and first one might be different. Their method is composed of trial, error, intuition, and legwork. The theorist, on the other hand, lies back in a hammock and deduces truths from certain basic postulates by a chain of pure logic which proves it for every case, without exception.

The Babylonians and Egyptians used empirical means exclusively, and they discovered a great deal of elementary mathematical truth by collecting myriads of examples over long periods of time. The theoretical method originated in Greece, where it came to full flower in Euclid's Elements about 300 B.C. You are familiar with it in geometry, which begins with certain terms, definitions, and postulates, then from these are deduced a chain of theorems. After the decline of Greek civilization it languished, and the empirical and practical prevailed for nearly two thousand years. But in the nineteenth century there began to be a revival of the classical ideal of precision and rigorous proof. Once more the tide turned toward logical purity and abstraction. We are now well into that period—the so-called modern mathematical method is the same deductive-postulational approach of the Greeks.

In keeping with this ideal, arithmetic and algebra are now organized into a theoretical structure like geometry. Such a Euclidean method calls for the setting down at the beginning of a few assertions that are assumed without proof, and then deducing everything else from them. The ACD laws are these assertions. They play the same role that the postulates, such as "All right angles are equal" and "Only one straight line can be drawn through two given points," do in geometry.

## The ACD Laws and Arithmetic

The simplest of these, stated in mathematical language, is the commutative property for addition: $a + b = b + a$. Done with numbers, $5 + 1 = 1 + 5$. Some books for the primary grades come right out and use the word. The Greater Cleveland Mathematics Program's text for first grade says, in a footnote marked with a picture of a key, "Addition is commutative." Most just impart the idea indirectly. The commutative property for multiplication, $ab = ba$, is handled similarly.

The law of association declares an equally obvious fact —that $2 + (3 + 4) = (2 + 3) + 4$. (Do the part in parentheses first and then add the other number.) Formally stated, the associative property for addition: $a + (b + c) = (a + b) + c$. It is necessary because addition, like marriage, is a binary operation—only two can take part in it at a time. To add three numbers, you first add any two of them, then add that answer to the third one. The law of association merely states what you already know— that it doesn't matter which two you add first.

This property plays a vital role in the way children are

now taught to add, as you can see in the following example:

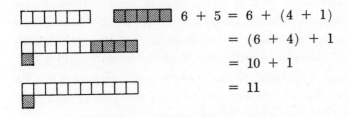

$$9 + 3 = 9 + (1 + 2)$$
$$= (9 + 1) + 2$$
$$= 10 + 2$$
$$= 12$$

They start with sets, regroup them by using the law of association, always building sets of ten, and then add as the union of sets. "We join sets, we add numbers," they say. In the Greater Cleveland Mathematics Program's text, grade one, $6 + 5$ is illustrated with sets of squares, one set white, one set blue:

$$6 + 5 = 6 + (4 + 1)$$
$$= (6 + 4) + 1$$
$$= 10 + 1$$
$$= 11$$

A great deal hinges on the child's ability to split the second number into two parts, one of which will combine with the first number to make ten. There are pages of practice on this, such as:

$$5 + 8 = 5 + \underline{\quad} + 3 = 10 + \square$$

(The vacant box, waiting to hold a numeral, is a device originated by the University of Illinois Arithmetic Project, which calls them frames. They come in several varieties—squares, triangles, lozenges, etc. A ground rule says that, in any one problem, you have to use the same number in every frame that is shaped alike. These frames play the same logical role as the letters of algebra, but have the advantage of eliciting the question, "What can go in the frame to make a true statement?" instead of, "What *is x?*" This is in line with current teaching, that a variable should be thought of as a sort of hole in the sentence, waiting to be filled in.)

Often the way has been prepared by using, in kindergarten, either the Cuisenaire rods or the blocks of Catherine Stern's *Structural Arithmetic*. The two systems are very similar, each consisting of a set of wooden pieces varying from one unit to ten units in length. Cuisenaire, a Belgian, used one centimeter as his unit; Catherine Stern, an American, uses ¾ inch, so hers are therefore larger throughout. Each introduces the child to numbers through measuring, rather than by counting, the traditional gateway to arithmetic. If Billy wants to find $3 + 2$, instead of counting 3 clowns here and 2 clowns there, he places the 3-block end-to-end with the 2-block and then finds the block whose length measures the same.

Both use a characteristic color for each number, but the two systems do not jibe—the Cuisenaire rod for 10 is orange, the Stern 10-block is blue. The children learn to identify the blocks both by length and color. If the blocks are piled up so that only part of the blue block is showing, Susie recognizes it as the 10-block by its color, although she can't see the full length. That is, she recognizes it as the 10-block if her kindergarten uses the Stern material. (What happens if Susie's father's company transfers him to another city in the middle of the school year and *that* kindergarten uses Cuisenaire rods? Then, when she pulls out the blue rod, it is the 9 and all her problems come out wrong. Probably this is just one of the hazards in the life of the family of the company man.)

The use of these rods and blocks is carried through the first and second grades—sometimes higher. This accords with current pedagogical procedure, which is to present number concepts first through physical operations with three-dimensional objects, follow this with two-dimensional marks on paper, and then proceed to traditional Hindu-Arabic numerals.

By grade two the children are handling sets of more than one ten—twenty, thirty, etc. (The objects in their sets have now lost some of their barnyard flavor—not so many baby ducks and frolicking lambs. The Indian phase has begun, with sets of tepees, papooses, and moccasins.) $22 + 4$ becomes $(20 + 2) + 4$, then $20 + (2 + 4)$ by the law of association, then $20 + 6$, and finally 26.

More complicated examples require the laws of both commutation and association.

$$
\begin{aligned}
23 + 30 &= (20 + 3) + 30 &&\text{(Because } 23 = 20 + 3\text{)} \\
&= 20 + (3 + 30) &&\text{(Addition is associative)} \\
&= 20 + (30 + 3) &&\text{(The commutative prop-} \\
& &&\text{erty permits the 3 and} \\
& &&\text{the 30 to change places)} \\
&= (20 + 30) + 3 &&\text{(Addition is associative)} \\
&= 50 + 3 &&\text{(}20 + 30 = 50\text{)} \\
&= 53
\end{aligned}
$$

Some books call this "scrambling." *The Math Workshop for Children* texts of the Encyclopaedia Britannica Films, Inc. call it the "in-any-order rule."

In the higher grades the problems get harder:

$$38 + 3 = (30 + 8) + 3$$
$$= 30 + (8 + 3)$$
$$= 30 + (8 + [2 + 1])$$
$$= 30 + ([8 + 2] + 1)$$
$$= 30 + (10 + 1)$$
$$= (30 + 10) + 1$$
$$= 40 + 1$$
$$= 41$$

True, nobody is going to go through life putting all this down whenever he wants to add. But this is the way people who add mentally have always worked—by thinking in groups of tens. They don't, in their mind's eye, put the 3 under the 8 in 38 and picture a little 1 carried to the top of the next column. Not if they're good, they don't. The old-fashioned skill of mental arithmetic is making a comeback in the new math. For example, the Ginn Arithmetic Enrichment Program, grade four, has pages of practice on mental addition. "Add the tens first," they say. You can see the advantage in a problem such as:

$$65 + 27 = (60 + 20) + (5 + 7)$$
$$= 80 + 12$$
$$= 92$$

As you probably surmised, there is also a law of association for multiplication. $(a \times b) \times c = a \times (b \times c)$. Changing partners does not affect the outcome, as you can tell by working out $(2 \times 3) \times 4$ and $2 \times (3 \times 4)$. This property enables a child to reduce a multiplication problem involving some fact he has not yet learned to one containing only known multiplication facts.

$$3 \times 20 = 3 \times (2 \times 10)$$
$$= (3 \times 2) \times 10$$
$$= 6 \times 10$$
$$= 60$$

The D in ACD stands for the law of distribution. You need this in problems where both addition and multiplication are involved. Formally stated, the distributive property is: $a \times (b + c) = (a \times b) + (a \times c)$. That is, 4 times $(2 + 3) = 4(2) + 4(3)$. Add 2 and 3, then multiply the answer by 4, and it's the same as multiplying each number separately by 4 and then adding.

Like the law of association, this property also provides a way to separate a new factor into two numbers that a child already knows how to multiply by, as in the following problem where 3 is changed to $2 + 1$.

$$2 \times 3 = 2 \times (2 + 1)$$
$$= (2 \times 2) + (2 \times 1)$$
$$= 4 + 2$$
$$= 6$$

(By the way, don't say "multiplier"—say "factor." If the vocabulary now used in many texts continues to be adopted, terms like multiplicand, multiplier, subtrahend, and minuend may soon become as old-fashioned as silk stockings. About the only word in that category still in good standing is addend, possibly because there isn't any good synonym for it. Oh yes, say "regroup" instead of "carry," too.) A problem that calls for multiplication by 4 could be changed to $3 + 1$, 5 to $3 + 2$, and so on, all the way up to 9 times 9.

In the fourth grade, the School Mathematics Study

Group's text shows two-digit multiplication handled the same way.

$$7 \times 18 = 7 \times (10 + 8)$$
$$= (7 \times 10) + (7 \times 8)$$
$$= 70 + 56$$
$$= 126$$

Any time you multiply by a two-digit number, you are using the law of distribution, although the traditional way of writing it somewhat conceals the fact.

$$
\begin{array}{r}
23 \\
\times\ 12 \\
\hline
46 \\
23\phantom{0} \\
\hline
276
\end{array}
$$

What you did was to take 2 times 23, making 46, a partial product, then 10 times 23, giving 230, the other partial product, and then add the two partial products. We move the "23" over one space to the left, showing there is really a zero after the "3," although it is invisible.

You better be prepared for the new way of doing long division that the textbooks are showing, too. The Scott Foresman series *Seeing Through Arithmetic* explains this method in the fourth and fifth grades. Suppose you want to divide 176 by 14. Start by estimating the number of times it will go. Say you guess 10.

$$
\begin{array}{r|l}
14)\ \overline{176} & 10 \\
140 & \\
\hline
36 & 2 \\
28 & \\
\hline
8 & 12
\end{array}
$$

Now guess how many times 14 will go into 36—probably 2. Add the two partial quotients. The answer is 12, with a remainder of 8. It wouldn't matter what you guessed first, as long as it wasn't too large—the answer would come out the same. The best first guess is 10 or some multiple of 10.

If the problem is 856 divided by 12, you, being very astute, would probably estimate that it will go 70 times. A fifth-grader might guess 50; a younger child would maybe guess 20. All three will turn out to have the same answer—71, remainder 4.

```
12) 856   70      12) 856   50      12) 856   20
    840                600              240
    ————  —          ————  ——          ————  ——
     16    1          256   20         616   30
     12               240              360
    ————  ——         ————  —          ————  ——
      4   71          16    1         256   20
                      12              240
                     ————  ——         ————  ——
                       4   71          16    1
                                       12
                                      ————  ——
                                        4   71
```

This saves all the erasing and starting over that comes with having to find an exact quotient on the first try.

In the lower grades the approach to the ACD laws is intuitive. They are beneath the surface—possibly printed in the margin of only the teacher's text—and it is their effects that you observe. The ideas are conveyed to the children in their language. *The Math Workshop for Children* calls the law of distribution the "Do-it-to-both rule." In two-digit multiplication, such as $(10 + 6)$ $(20 + 3)$, it is the "Double-do-it-to-both rule." But by the last part of the sixth grade—sometimes sooner—the technical names for these principles are unveiled.

In the seventh grade of the SMSG program these whisperings of mathematics to come are brought out in the open. The laws of association, commutation, and distribution are explicitly written down in mathematical language. Since many of the students learned grade-school arithmetic with emphasis on manipulation and little, if any, attention paid to structure, the structure of arithmetic is presented again in preparation for the transition into algebra. The problems, naturally, are harder than for the younger children, as you see here:

$$(44 \times 24) + (12 \times 12)$$
$$(44 \times 2 \times 12) + (12 \times 12)$$
$$(88 \times 12) + (12 \times 12)$$
$$12 (88 + 12)$$
$$12 (100)$$
$$1200$$

This, of course, is a trick example, meant to convey the idea that regrouping can provide a short cut so that the problem can be done mentally.

### PROBLEMS

Which of the following statements are true? For those which are true, name the law involved:

1. $(3 + 2) + 5 = (2 + 3) + 5$
2. $4 + (3 \times 5) = (4 + 3) \times (4 + 5)$
3. $4 + (3 + 1) = (4 + 3) + 1$
4. $8 \times 3 = 3 \times 8$
5. $4 - 6 = 6 - 4$
6. $3 \times (6 + 5) = (3 \times 6) + 5$

7. $2 \times (4 \times 6) = (2 \times 4) \times 6$
8. $6(2 + 5) = [6(2)] + [6(5)]$
9. $(12 \div 3) \div 2 = 3 \div (12 \div 2)$
10. $(9 + 14) \times (23 + 5) = [(9 + 14) \times 23] +$
$[(9 + 14) \times 5]$

## OTHER NUMBER PROPERTIES

Closure has already been mentioned in the chapter on number systems. It is, simply, the property of remaining closed, which a given set of numbers may (or may not) possess when a certain operation is performed on some of its members. For instance, the set of whole numbers is closed under addition. Add any two whole numbers and the answer is again a whole number—a member of the original set. The same is true of multiplication, but if you divide you may get a fraction, as in $2 \div 7$. $\frac{2}{7}$ is not a member of the set of whole numbers—it is an outsider. Therefore, the set of whole numbers possesses the property of closure under addition or multiplication, but not under division.

Zero and one have special properties which the other numbers lack. Zero is the identity element for addition—add it to any number and the sum is that same number. In symbols, $a + 0 = a$. 1 serves the same purpose in multiplication—multiply any number by 1 and the answer is the original number, that is, $a \times 1 = a$.

The existence of these identity elements gives meaning to the idea of an inverse. $-2$ is the additive inverse of 2 because their sum is 0. This leads to the concept of subtraction as the inverse operation to addition. One undoes the other. Instead of subtracting, the same result can be obtained by adding the inverse element. For example, $6 + (-2)$ is exactly the same as subtracting 2 from 6. Therefore the idea of subtraction as a separate operation can be done away with entirely.

In the same way the multiplicative inverse of a number is that number by which you can multiply it to make 1. The multiplicative inverse of 5 is $\frac{1}{5}$, because their product is 1. The other name for it is reciprocal. Every rational number, except 0, has exactly one reciprocal, which you can find by turning its fraction upside down. $\frac{4}{3}$ is the reciprocal of $\frac{3}{4}$, and vice versa.

Division is the inverse operation to multiplication. You actually use it to answer the question "By what must I multiply?" In a division problem you are given one factor and the product—you have to find the other factor. You can do this by multiplying by the reciprocal. In fact, you are accustomed to doing this with fractions, because of the old rule "To divide by a fraction, invert and multiply." In the problem $\frac{4}{5} \div \frac{2}{3}$ you automatically put $\frac{4}{5} \times \frac{3}{2}$ and come out with $\frac{12}{10}$ or $1\frac{1}{5}$. But why? In the SMSG text for the fifth grade and other similar books a logic behind this rule is explained.

$\frac{4}{5} \div \frac{2}{3}$ really means $\frac{2}{3} \times ? = \frac{4}{5}$. To find the ?, you could reason as follows, with one of the ACD laws or number properties to back you up at every step:

$$1 \times \frac{4}{5} = \frac{4}{5} \text{ (1 is the multiplicative identity)}$$
$$\frac{2}{3} \times \frac{3}{2} = 1 \text{ (multiplicative inverse)}$$

Therefore you can substitute $(\frac{2}{3} \times \frac{3}{2})$ for the 1 in the first equation and you have:

$$( \tfrac{2}{3} \times \tfrac{3}{2} ) \times \tfrac{4}{5} = \tfrac{4}{5}$$
$$\tfrac{2}{3} \times ( \tfrac{3}{2} \times \tfrac{4}{5} ) = \tfrac{4}{5}$$

(Law of Association for Multiplication)

This is just like $\tfrac{2}{3} \times ? = \tfrac{4}{5}$, with ? replaced by $( \tfrac{3}{2} \times \tfrac{4}{5} )$. When you find out what $\tfrac{3}{2} \times \tfrac{4}{5}$ is, you will have found the number that must replace the ?.

Looking at it this way, we can get rid of division as an operation in its own right, since to divide by a number you can always multiply by its reciprocal. $12 \div 4$ is the same as $12 \times \tfrac{1}{4}$. This leaves only two basic operations—addition and multiplication. They possess the commutative and associative properties while the inverse operations—subtraction and division—do not. $6 - 2$ is not the same as $2 - 6$. Neither is $6 \div 2$ the same as $2 \div 6$. $(5 - 3) - 2$ does not equal $5 - (3 - 2)$, either, nor does $(6 \div 2) \div 3$ equal $6 \div (2 \div 3)$.

When all the layers of flash cards and drill books are scraped away and the underlying mathematical bones of arithmetic exposed, you will see that they consist of the following:

Closure Law for Addition
Closure Law for Multiplication
Commutative Law for Addition
Commutative Law for Multiplication
Associative Law for Addition
Associative Law for Multiplication
Identity Law for Addition
Identity Law for Multiplication
Inverse Law for Addition
Inverse Law for Multiplication
Distributive Law

These eleven laws form the foundation of the entire subject of arithmetic.

1. Give the additive inverse of each of the following: 3, ½, 1, −2, −⅘

2. Give the multiplicative inverse of each number in problem 1.

Name the law that is illustrated by each of the following:

   3. $6 \times \frac{1}{6} = 1$
   4. $5 + 0 = 5$
   5. $3 + (-3) = 0$
   6. $4 \times 1 = 4$

## THE ACD AND OTHER LAWS IN ALGEBRA

Algebra is now taught as a study of the structure of a mathematical system, rather than a kind of symbolized arithmetic using letters instead of numbers, which was the old way. Proof plays a large part in today's algebra course, whereas you probably studied it only in geometry. The central idea in a logical structure, in the mathematical sense, is that some statements are consequences of other statements. This is succinctly called "if-then thinking." To prove a statement that is in the form "If $A$, then $B$" you have to construct a chain of reasons leading from $A$ to $B$, and the reasons must be chosen from the basic properties of the system.

The eleven laws listed for arithmetic also hold for algebra. Add to these a few axioms which you may remember from geometry, such as "A quantity may be substituted for its equal in any expression without changing the value of the expression" (in the more precise language of today, "The name for any number may be replaced by any other name for the same number without affecting the meaning"), or "If the same quantity is added to equal quantities, the sums are equal" and you are equipped to prove a few theorems in algebra. It is not a proof, of course, if there is a loophole in it—every step must be legal. (If you are a lawyer, this should be your meat.) Try this:

To prove:   $(a - b) + b = a$
Proof:
$$(a - b) + b = [a + (-b)] + b = a + (-b + b)$$
$$\text{Law of Association}$$
$$-b + b = 0 \quad \text{Additive inverse}$$
$$(a - b) + b = a + 0 \quad \text{Substitution}$$
$$(a - b) + b = a \quad \text{Additive identity}$$

Or this:

To prove: $(a + b)(c + d) = ac + bc + ad + bd$
Proof:
$$(a + b)(c + d) = [(a + b)c] + [(a + b)d] \quad \text{Law of Distribution}$$
$$= [c(a + b)] + [d(a + b)] \quad \text{Commutative property of multiplication}$$
$$= [(ca) + (cb)] + [(da) + (db)] \quad \text{Law of Distribution}$$
$$= [(ac) + (bc)] + [(ad) + (bd)] \quad \text{Commutative property of multiplication}$$
$$= [(ac) + (bc) + (ad)] + (bd) \quad \text{Associative property of addition}$$
$$= (ac) + (bc) + (ad) + (bd) \quad \text{or}$$
$$= ac + bc + ad + bd \quad \text{Convention of performing multiplication before addition}$$

A problem involving the two negative signs is trickier:

To prove: $-(-a) = a$

Proof: $-a$ exists    Additive inverse

$-(-a) + (-a) = 0$    Additive inverse

$[-(-a) + (-a)] + a = 0 + a$    Addition axiom

$[-(-a) + (-a)] + a = a$    Identity element in addition

$-(-a) + [(-a) + a] = a$    Law of Association for addition

$[(-a) + a] = 0$    Additive inverse

$-(-a) + 0 = a$    Substitution

$-(-a) = a$    Identity element in addition

### Problems

1. Prove that $(2a + 3b) + (5a + 7b) = 7a + 10b$
2. Prove that $ab + ac + ad = a(b + c + d)$
3. Prove that $(a + 2b)(2a + b) = 2a^2 + 5ab + 2b^2$

## Mathematical Systems

What is a mathematical system? It is a set of objects together with one or more operations which can be performed on them. A table really describes a mathematical system. If you study an ordinary multiplication table—say the fives—it tells you many things besides the answer to 5 times 5.

| × | 1 | 2 | 3 | 4 | 5 |
|---|---|---|---|---|---|
| 1 | 1 | 2 | 3 | 4 | 5 |
| 2 | 2 | 4 | 6 | 8 | 10 |
| 3 | 3 | 6 | 9 | 12 | 15 |
| 4 | 4 | 8 | 12 | 16 | 20 |
| 5 | 5 | 10 | 15 | 20 | 25 |

The objects in this mathematical system are the natural numbers 1 through 5. The set is obviously not closed, since many other numbers appear as the result of the operation, multiplication. Test it to see if it has the commutative property. The easiest way is to draw the diagonal from $\times$ to 25. If the table is symmetric with respect to this diagonal—that is, if you folded it along the diagonal and the numbers on the two sides were exactly the same, 20 falling on top of 20, 4 on top of 4, etc.—then the system is commutative.

Does it have an identity element? Even if you didn't already know that 1 times any number leaves it unchanged, you could tell 1 was the identity element from the fact that its row is just a copy of the column headings, and a similar remark holds for its column.

Is there an inverse for every object in the set? No—there's nothing in the set to multiply 2 by and get the identity element. You can tell that in a minute by just looking down the column headed "2." "1" does not appear; therefore there is no inverse element for 2. Neither is there one for 3, 4, or 5 because there is no 1 in their columns, either. The test for the inverse property is simple in terms of the table. It is just the requirement that the identity element appear in every column.

To give more insight into the structure of a mathematical system, the School Mathematics Study Group, in grade seven, introduces systems other than those of ordinary arithmetic—for instance, the modulo systems.

Here is the multiplication table, modulo 5, which was explained in Chapter III:

| × | 0 | 1 | 2 | 3 | 4 |
|---|---|---|---|---|---|
| 0 | 0 | 0 | 0 | 0 | 0 |
| 1 | 0 | 1 | 2 | 3 | 4 |
| 2 | 0 | 2 | 4 | 1 | 3 |
| 3 | 0 | 3 | 1 | 4 | 2 |
| 4 | 0 | 4 | 3 | 2 | 1 |

If you analyze its structure the same way you did the one above, you see that it has the property of closure. Every object that appears is one of the numbers in the set {0,1,2,3,4}. The diagonal test shows that it is a commutative system. Look for the row which is a copy of the column headings and you see that 1 is the identity element. This element appears in every column, except zero's; therefore every number except zero has a multiplicative inverse.

Custom and tradition dictate that the objects in a mathematical system be numbers, and that the operations be addition and multiplication, but they don't *have* to be. Let's take four letters as objects and * as an undefined operation. From the table below you can deduce several facts about this unknown system.

| * | a | b | c | d |
|---|---|---|---|---|
| a | c | d | a | b |
| b | d | a | b | c |
| c | a | b | c | d |
| d | b | c | d | a |

It's handy to have a name to call an undefined operation. The SMSG suggests "twiddle." Instead of saying, "Add $a$ and $b$" or "Multiply $a$ and $b$," say "Twiddle $a$ and $b$." On the table above, the answer you get from twiddling $a$ and $b$ is $d$. Twiddle $d$ and $c$ and the answer is $d$. This gives you a clue that $c$ might be the identity element. Look at $c$'s row and column and you see that it is, indeed, a copy of the column heading, therefore $c$ *is* the identity element.

The table is symmetric with respect to the diagonal, so you know the operation of twiddling possesses the commutative property. Because $c$, the identity element, appears in every column, you also know that every element has an inverse. For instance, $d$'s inverse is $b$, since the answer to twiddling $d$ and $b$ is $c$. Finally, the only elements appearing on the table are $a$, $b$, $c$, and $d$, therefore the system is closed under twiddling.

The point to all this is that you were able to find out these things about the structure of this unknown mathematical system without knowing what $a$, $b$, $c$, $d$, and $*$ are.

### PROBLEMS

Answer each of the following questions for the tables given below:

1. Do the operations possess the commutative property?

2. Is the system closed under the operation?

3. Does the system have an identity element? If so, what is it?

4. Does each element have an inverse? If so, name each one.

TABLE A

| + | 0 | 1 | 2 |
|---|---|---|---|
| 0 | 0 | 1 | 2 |
| 1 | 1 | 2 | 0 |
| 2 | 2 | 0 | 1 |

TABLE B

| + | 2 | 4 | 6 |
|---|---|---|---|
| 2 | 4 | 6 | 8 |
| 4 | 6 | 8 | 10 |
| 6 | 8 | 10 | 12 |

TABLE C

| × | 1 | 3 | 5 |
|---|---|---|---|
| 1 | 1 | 3 | 5 |
| 3 | 3 | 9 | 15 |
| 5 | 5 | 15 | 25 |

TABLE D

| * | e | a | b | c |
|---|---|---|---|---|
| e | e | a | b | c |
| a | a | e | c | b |
| b | b | c | e | a |
| c | c | b | a | e |

# Inequalities 6

Equations, I'm sure, are familiar to you, but are you prepared for inequations? This term is used in the texts of the University of Illinois Committee on School Mathematics. Most books say inequalities, but, either way, they look like this: $x + 4 > 6$. The symbol ">" means "is greater than." Think of a number which, added to 4, will give a sum greater than 6. Obviously, anything larger than 2 will do. Therefore we have, not one answer, but a set of answers—the solution set. It is written, in the case of the problem above, $x > 2$. If you want to use set notation, then you could write {All numbers greater than 2} or $\{x \mid x > 2\}$, see Chapter II. Turn ">" around and "<" means "is less than." (The symbol always points toward the smaller quantity.) If $x + 2 < 7$, the solution set would be $x < 5$.

Inequalities were one of the first of the new math topics to be incorporated into the curriculum. The College Board Commission on Mathematics published in 1958 a pamphlet *Concepts of Equation and Inequality* intended as a supplementary unit that could be used with the traditional texts, which were the only ones available at that time. Soon afterward, most textbooks added a chapter on this subject.

The ideas and symbols of inequality are now taught in every grade from the first on up. The University of Illinois Arithmetic Project uses exercises such as these in the first grade: $\square > 3; 4 + 2 > \square$ . (This calls for an appropriate numeral to be put in the box.) The Greater Cleveland Mathematics Program for the first grade asks the children to "Write the correct sign $>$, $<$, or $=$, in the $\bigcirc$ : $2 + 2 \bigcirc 5$." In the second grade the directions are the same, but the problem is harder: "$32 + 4 \bigcirc 30 + 7$." By the third grade it is "$329,971 \bigcirc 429,871$."

The Ginn Arithmetic Enrichment Program in the fourth grade uses the inequality symbols in problems comparing fractions and measures, such as $\frac{7}{8} > \frac{5}{8}$, and 2 gals. $> 10$ pts. Fifth-graders are asked to judge the truth or falseness of statements like: "$\frac{3}{6} - \frac{1}{6} > \frac{1}{3}$." The sixth-grade text includes problems where the pupil is asked to "Fill in each blank with the symbol $>$ or $<$: $(\frac{1}{2})^3$ ___ $\frac{1}{2}$."

### GRAPHING THE SOLUTION SET ON A NUMBER LINE

In junior high school, equations and inequalities are presented together—they are both called open sentences. Whether you say: "The _____ won the pennant in 1962," or: "__ $+ 9 = 14$" or: "$2 + __ > 5$," the idea is the same. Fill in the blank so as to make a true statement. The solution set (also called truth set) of the first sentence is, too obviously, {Yankees}, of the second, {5}, and of the third, {All numbers greater than 3}.

The solution to the equation, which was 5, could be shown on a number line simply by a dot at "5." The solution set of the inequality takes a little more work and looks like this:

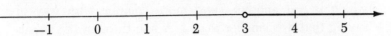

The arrow means that the line continues to the right. The heavily shaded part is the graph of the solution set—the fact that the circle at 3 is left open means that 3 is not included in the set. Only numbers larger than 3, such as $3\frac{1}{4}$, 4, $4\frac{1}{2}$, etc., will make the open sentence $2 + \underline{\quad} > 5$ true.

If the original problem had read $2 + \underline{\quad} \geqq 5$, meaning that $2 + \underline{\quad}$ was either equal to 5 or greater than 5, then the circle at 3 on the number line would also have been shaded, indicating that the solution set was: {3 and all numbers greater than 3}.

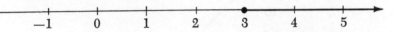

For convenience, $x$'s soon replace the blanks. The problem above could just as well have been written $2 + x \geqq 5$, and the solution, $x \geqq 3$.

A more complicated example, like $x^2 > 9$, has a graph in two parts, to match its two-part solution, that $x$ is either greater than 3 or less than $-3$.

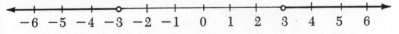

A line drawn through the symbol has the effect of inserting a "not" in the wording. $x \not> 5$ says that $x$ is not

greater than 5—it is either less than 5 or equal to 5.
$x \nleq 4$ means that $x$ is not equal to or greater than 4,
which is just another (and more complicated) way of
saying that it is smaller than 4. A line through the equals
sign, as in $x \neq 2$, specifies that $x$ and 2 are unequal, but
does not tell you which is larger. Any number, other than
2, would be a solution to the problem.

Some inequalities have no answer at all, for example
$8 + x \leq x$. In that case, the solution is the empty set,
and if you are asked to draw a graph, just *don't* draw
anything.

PROBLEMS

Find the solution set of each of the following open sentences. Graph the first four on the number line:

1. $x + 5 > 7$
2. $x^2 > 16$
3. $x < -2$
4. $x + 3 \geq 2$
5. $x \nleq -7$
6. $x \geq x + 6$
7. $2 + 7 \neq x + 2$
8. $x + 4 \nleq 8$
9. $x + 5 = 3 + x$
10. $0 \leq x \leq 5$

## AXIOMS OF INEQUALITIES

In first-year algebra, whether taught in the eighth or
ninth grade, part of the course consists of the theory and
practice of solving inequalities, as well as equations. The
theory requires certain axioms, or principles of inequality,

which are much the same as the axioms of inequality which have always been a part of plane geometry.

One of these is: If the same number is added to both members of an inequality, the results are unequal in the same order. Expressed more compactly in symbols: If $a > b$, then $a + c > b + c$. A numerical example, such as this, makes it obvious:

$$12 > 5$$
$$12 + 3 > 5 + 3$$
$$15 > 8$$

Since subtraction can be treated as the addition of an inverse, a separate axiom for subtraction is unnecessary. That is, you can always add a $-3$ instead of subtracting $+ 3$, and come out the same. Similarly, you can get around dividing by multiplying by a reciprocal, so there is no need for a separate division axiom, either. The following two axioms for multiplication take care of the matter:

1. If unequal numbers are multiplied by the same *positive* number, the results are unequal in the *same* order.

2. If unequal numbers are multiplied by the same *negative* number, the results are unequal in *reverse* order.

The first part is easy to see.

$$6 > 4$$
$$2(6) > 2(4)$$
$$12 > 8$$

It's the second part that is tricky.

$$6 > -1$$
$$-2(6) \ ? \ -2(-1)$$
$$-12 \ ? \ 2$$

Obviously —12 is not greater than 2; it's less than 2, so the inequality symbol has to be turned around.

These axioms are applied in solving problems in inequalities, such as the following:

$$1. \quad 2x - 7 > 15$$
$$2x > 22 \quad \text{(Add 7 to both members. Addition Axiom)}$$
$$x > 11 \quad \text{(Multiply both members by } \tfrac{1}{2}. \text{ First Multiplication Axiom)}$$

To check your work, take a number greater than 11, such as 12.

$$2(12) - 7 > 15$$
$$24 - 7 > 15$$
$$17 > 15$$

$$2. \quad 28 - 4x < 8$$
$$-4x < -20 \quad \text{(Add } -28 \text{ to both members. Addition Axiom)}$$
$$x > 5 \quad \text{(Multiply both members by } -\tfrac{1}{4}. \text{ Second Multiplication Axiom. Notice the reversed order of inequality.)}$$

To test your answer, take a number greater than 5, such as 6:

$$28 - 4(6) < 8$$
$$28 - 24 < 8$$
$$4 < 8$$

Look at what would happen if you hadn't turned the inequality sign around and came out with a number smaller than 5. Test 4:

$$28 - 4(4) < 8$$
$$28 - 16 < 8$$
$$12 < 8 \quad \text{This is obviously not true.}$$

Problems with the combined symbol "$\geqq$" or "$\leqq$" are worked the same way:

$$3x - 2 \leqq 10 - x$$

$4x - 2 \leqq 10$      (Add $x$ to each member. Addition Axiom for inequalities)

$4x \leqq 12$      (Add 2 to each member. Addition Axiom for inequalities)

$x \leqq 3$      (Multiply each member by $\frac{1}{4}$. Multiplication Axiom for inequalities)

To check your answer, split it into two parts, $x = 3$, and $x < 3$. For the first part:

$$3(3) - 2 = 10 - (3)$$
$$9 - 2 = 10 - 3$$
$$7 = 7$$

Select a number from the solution set of the second part—for instance, 2:

$$3(2) - 2 < 10 - (2)$$
$$6 - 2 < 10 - 2$$
$$4 < 6$$

### PROBLEMS

Solve the following inequalities:

1. $4x - 2 < 10$
2. $x + 5 > 7$
3. $3 + x \leqq 2$
4. $8 - 2x < 14$
5. $6x - 3 < x + 2$
6. $4x + 3 \geqq 7x - 12$

### GRAPHING IN A PLANE

Just as in equations, you may have inequalities with two variables, $x$ and $y$, instead of just one. These are most easily analyzed by means of a graph. Since you have two dimensions to picture, a one-dimensional line won't do. It takes a plane—the same Cartesian plane you used for graphing equations when you took algebra.

In the problem $x + y > 3$, start by finding out where the line $x + y = 3$ would go on the graph. Make a table of ordered pairs that fit the equation:

| $x$ | 1 | 0 | 2 |
|-----|---|---|---|
| $y$ | 2 | 3 | 1 |

Actually, two pairs are enough, since it only takes two points to determine a straight line. This line separates the points in the plane into three sets—a set of points on the line, a set of points on one side of the line, and a set of points on the other side of the line. The set on the line (the ones in the table above and many others) satisfy the equation. However, we are not graphing it, so make the line dotted. Of the other two sets, one will fit the inequality $x + y > 3$ and the other will fit $x + y < 3$. Your only problem is to decide which is which. Pick a pair of numbers that fulfill the conditions stated in the inequality—for instance, $x = 2$, $y = 4$. Locate that point and see which side of the dotted line it falls on. Try a few more if you want to—they will all fall on the same side of the line. The coordinates of every point in this half plane satisfy the inequality $x + y > 3$, so indicate this fact by shading it in.

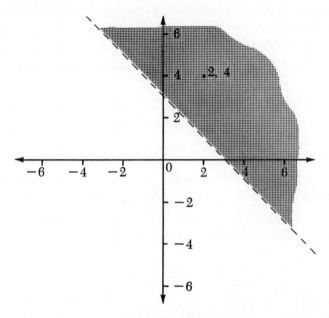

Had you drawn the line solid, instead of dotted, it would show that the points *on* the line were also included in the graph. This would be the case if the problem had been $x + y \geqq 3$.

If several inequalities are graphed simultaneously on the same plane, their common solution will show up in the overlapping of the different shaded areas. This is often a triangle, quadrilateral, or some other polygon, and for that reason is called a polygonal convex set. Linear programming problems (practical problems where certain limitations are placed on the variables), which are in-

cluded in courses for the eleventh and twelfth grades, can be solved in this way. Take the following example:

A manufacturer is planning to buy some new machines. There are two models that will fit his needs. He wants at least 2 of Model X and at least 1 of Model Y. His floor space will accommodate only 6 machines. The dealer can supply 4 Model X's and 3 Model Y's. How many of each should he buy for maximum output, if Model X can manufacture 600 gadgets a day and Model Y can manufacture 500 gadgets a day?

From the conditions given you can set up the inequalities, letting $x$ = the number of Model X machines he should buy, and $y$ = the number of Model Y's. Since he will buy at least 2 of Model X, then $x$ either equals 2 or is greater than 2. Write this in symbols as:

$$x \geqq 2$$

Similarly, because he will buy at least 1 of Model Y:

$$y \geqq 1$$

Graph each of these two inequalities by the method explained above, putting them both on the same plane.

You also know that the sum of the two models will be 6 or less, because the floor space will only accommodate that many. Express this algebraically as:

$$x + y \leqq 6$$

and graph it on the same plane as the other two.

The conditions about the number the dealer can supply give you the facts that the number of Model $X$'s must be 4 or less, written as:

$$x \leqq 4$$

and the number of Model $Y$'s is 3 or less, written:

$$y \leqq 3$$

Graph these two inequalities also on the same plane and you have this:

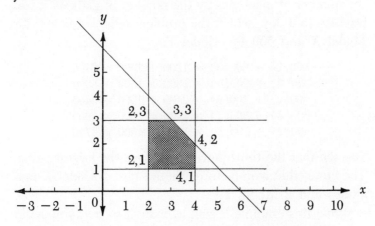

For purposes of clarification I have shaded in only the overlapping areas—otherwise there would be a welter of five different kinds of cross-hatching, one to go with each of the five lines graphed. Any point in this shaded region or on its boundaries represents a pair of numbers that will fit the conditions laid down in the problem. The question now is: Which one of these pairs will give the manufacturer maximum output?

It can be proved (but beyond the scope of this book)

that the maximum occurs at a vertex of the polygon, therefore the answer will be one of the five number pairs which you see at the vertices of the figure on the graph above. Bearing in mind that in graphing the $x$ is always named first, you now know that the five possibilities are: 2 Model $X$ machines and 3 Model $Y$; 3 Model $X$ and 3 Model $Y$; 4 Model $X$ and 2 Model $Y$; etc.

Test these five possibilities by multiplying, in each case, the number of machines by the number of gadgets it can produce in a day, which the problem tells you is 600 for Model $X$ and 500 for Model $Y$.

$$600(2) + 500(3) = 1200 + 1500 = 2700$$
$$600(3) + 500(3) = 1800 + 1500 = 3300$$
$$600(4) + 500(2) = 2400 + 1000 = 3400$$
$$600(4) + 500(1) = 2400 + \phantom{0}500 = 2900$$
$$600(2) + 500(1) = 1200 + \phantom{0}500 = 1700$$

You see that the third pair tested gives the largest value. Therefore, the manufacturer should buy 4 Model $X$ machines and 2 Model $Y$.

While this example is simple enough so that you could guess the answer without going through all the steps, in actual practice linear programming problems generally require computer solution because of their size.

### PROBLEMS

Joe, a college student, takes two courses that require a lot of time—Esperanto and Early Egyptian plumbing. (The rest of his schedule is a snap.) The Esperanto department requires that at least 5 hours a week be spent in the language laboratory, which is open from 2:00 to 5:00 o'clock Monday through Friday, inclusive. An enterprising former student has figured out that, on the average, each hour spent per week in the lab adds 5 points to the grade in the course. The Egyptian Museum's rare specimen room is open from 2:00 until 4:00 o'clock on Monday, Wednesday, and Saturday. Mr. Cxyzptv, who teaches Early Egyp. Plumb., estimates that each half-hour per week spent there is worth 4 points on a student's grade. If Joe, after allowing time for his necessities, duties, and pleasures, has a total of 17 hours a week to spend on the two courses, how can he best divide his time between them in order to secure maximum returns for his work?

# Geometry

If they're learning the binary system in arithmetic, and algebra problems now look like this: $(A \cap B)' = (A \cap B') \cup (A' \cap B) \cup (A' \cap B')$, what's happening to geometry? Plenty. It may have been Euclid alone who looked on beauty bare, as Edna St. Vincent Millay said, but nowadays a lot of other people are helping him. The modern point of view is not geometry, but geometries, including the non-Euclidean. For instance, there is projective geometry in which the figures are pictured as if drawn on a slide and thrown on a flat screen from various angles. The idea is to find what properties remain unchanged throughout these distortions. In topology—a geometry of form without size or shape—we go much, much farther. Some of the figures, as if made of rubber, are continuously deformed by stretching, squeezing, and twisting until any semblance of their original appearance is lost. A circle, deprived of its roundness, might look like this:

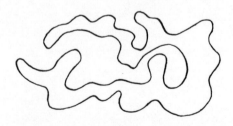

About the only property that's left is that it has an inside and an outside, although it's a little hard to tell which is which.

To get all this into the curriculum you have to start earlier. Patrick Suppes and Newton Hawley think second grade is not a bit too soon, judging from experimental work they did with children at Stanford Elementary School (a public school in the Palo Alto Unified School District) in 1958 and 1959. These were whole classes of first-, second-, and third-grade pupils—not just the gifted —who had geometry 15 minutes a day. Because of the positive results of this experiment (supported by grants from the Carnegie Corporation of New York and the National Science Foundation), they have written a text *Geometry for Primary Grades* to be used by seven- and eight-year-old children.

This book begins: "Draw many lines. Draw some long lines." and goes on through: "How many sides does a triangle have?" to: "Draw circles about the quadrilaterals. *Only* the quadrilaterals." (Yes, it has big words.) By chapter three these little children are bisecting line segments with straight-edge and compasses (sharp-pointed?). This classic construction is done without any reference to arithmetic—to bisect a six-inch segment it is not legal to divide six by two and then measure off three inches. A straight-edge, the accepted geometric tool, is not marked into inches, centimeters, or any other unit of measure. Here second-graders, unaccustomed to dividing, might have the advantage over older pupils in grasping the idea of pure geometry, which is independent of the arithmetic of measurement.

The traditional account of the origin of geometry is that

the Egyptians were obliged to invent it because of practical matters involving real estate taxes. Herodotus, the historian, says that the king divided the land among the Egyptians, giving each one an equal-sized piece, and levied taxes accordingly. Each year, at the flooding of the Nile, some of the land was torn away. When the owners notified the king, he sent surveyors to measure what was left and adjusted the taxes proportionally.

By Plato's time, the character of geometry had changed. In the *Republic*, after pointing out that it was ludicrous to call the subject land-measuring, he writes of geometers:

> I think you know that although they use visible figures and argue about them, they are not thinking about these figures but of those things which the figures represent; thus it is the square in itself and the diameter in itself which are the matter of their arguments, not that which they draw; similarly, when they model or draw objects . . . they use them in turn as images, endeavoring to see those absolute objects which cannot be seen otherwise than by thought.

This is precisely the viewpoint that the intuitive and informal geometry taught in the middle grades is meant to foster. The Ginn Arithmetic Enrichment Program fourth-grade text says, "Points and lines are only ideas. They may be represented with dots and marks on paper."

All the textbooks for these grades contain far more geometric material than formerly. Why? Primarily to give the pupils a background of facts and language for the geometry which they will have later. The concepts and definitions they learn here are the same ones to which they will refer in junior and senior high school.

Part of this background is developed by calling the students' attention to the models of geometric figures which are everywhere. The end of a drinking straw suggests a circle; a sheet of paper, a plane. A tennis ball represents a sphere and a can of soup serves as a cylinder. Hold a piece of string taut between your two hands and you are demonstrating a line segment.

By the way, when they bring you their homework, bear in mind that a line has *no* endpoints, but may extend indefinitely in each direction; a line *segment* has *two* endpoints, and a ray has *one* endpoint (the side of an angle is an example of a ray). A line segment can be measured, but a line cannot, since it has no beginning or end. Neither can a ray, since it has no end, only a beginning. A ray without its endpoint is a half line.

Line      Line Segment      Ray

These may (or may not) be marked with arrows. Just remember that if there is no point there to stop it, the line keeps on going, although only part of it can be shown on the paper.

The students' background is further developed by practice in comparing geometric figures. They begin with line segments, measured first with string and then with compasses. Angles are compared to each other and to a right angle. By the fifth and sixth grades, this leads to work on the congruence of triangles, specifically the case where three sides are given.

To develop an intuitive sense of size, a great deal of free use of estimation is used, followed by actual measurement. The children are usually surprised to find that doubling both the length and width of a rectangle makes the area not twice but four times as big. (So are some older students.)

## TOPOLOGY

If you see mention of the Jordan curve and the four-color map problem, this does not refer to the Middle Eastern political situation, as you might suppose. They are talking about topology, a new branch of mathematics whose growth has been phenomenal. Monsieur Jordan, a French mathematician, stated the following fundamental theorem of the subject: A simple closed curve in the plane divides the plane into exactly two regions, one inside the curve and one outside. Even if the plane is a sheet of rubber that is drastically deformed by stretching, shrinking, or twisting (everything is fair except tearing), this property persists. A simple closed curve remains a simple closed curve under all topological transformations.

Since this concept is basic to topology, the SMSG text introduces it in grade four. The phrase "simple closed curve" is rather misleading. "Closed" is straightforward enough—that just means it ends at the same point it started from. But "simple," used in this mathematical sense, means that it does not intersect itself. The diagram at the beginning of this chapter is a simple closed curve, but the following is not:

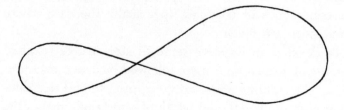

Neither does "curve" mean that the line can't be straight. Triangles, squares—in fact, all the polygons—are simple closed curves. Since the figures are distorted at will, straightness or curvature are only temporary properties of the line segment and have nothing to do with the underlying truth of the theorems.

By the sixth grade, the SMSG text carries this idea into three dimensions. A simple closed surface is a space figure which does not intersect itself and which divides the space in which it lies into an interior and an exterior. Think of a single soap bubble—its iridescent film is a model of a simple closed surface.

As to the four-color map problem, it is this: Suppose you are making a map, either flat or on a globe, and, as is customary, you want to use different colors for adjoining countries, so the boundaries will show up. What is the least number of colors you can get by with? Since the size and shape of the countries have nothing to do with the problem and only the position matters, it properly belongs in topology, another name for which is *analysis situs*— Latin for the study of position.

No map has ever been found that requires more than four colors, but neither have the topologists arrived at a proof for this fact. They *have* been able to prove that five will always suffice, however. Since there is neither a proof for a four-color theorem nor a counterexample disproving it, the matter is hanging fire at present. Try to find one or the other, if you want to.

Although topology is a creation of the last hundred years, there were a few isolated earlier discoveries, notably by the Swiss mathematician Leonhard Euler. His solution of the Seven Bridges of Königsberg problem, made when he was court mathematician to Frederick the Great, is one of the foundation stones of topology.

This problem—a famous one in his day—is about the seven bridges connecting an island at the forks of the river Pregel, the two river banks, and the land between the forks, located as you see in this diagram.

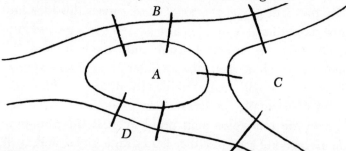

The townspeople of Königsberg (now Kaliningrad, since the Russians took over that part of Germany after World War II) amused themselves by trying to take a walk in such a way that they crossed each bridge once and only once. Some said it was impossible, some were doubtful, but Euler found no one who had actually done it. (The SMSG seventh-grade text includes this problem as a mathematical recreation.)

Theoretically you could solve it by listing all possible routes over the seven bridges and seeing if any fit the conditions, but that would be extremely long and tedious, because there are a very large number of possible combinations. Euler looked for a way of analyzing the problem first to see whether a solution was possible. He did this by replacing the four land areas by points A, B, C, D and the bridges by lines connecting them. Although there is no such drawing in his memoir on the subject, you *could* make a diagram something like this to represent the situation:

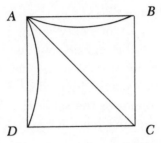

Of course, this doesn't look at all like an actual map of Königsberg. The real size and shape of either the island, the river, or the bridges has nothing to do with it. What the diagram shows is the fact that there are five bridges leading to A (the island) and three bridges to each of the other pieces of land—B, C, and D.

The problem then reduces to the question of whether you can trace this diagram in one swoop, without lifting your pencil from the paper or recrossing your path. If you can, the puzzle is solvable; if you can't, it is impossible. Silver-Burdette's text for the seventh grade has diagram puzzles similar to this, which the children work by trial and error. Euler found the underlying mathematical principle. If every vertex has an even number of lines converging there, the problem can be solved. It can also be solved if there are two vertices where an odd number of lines meet, but if there are more than two such odd vertices, the problem is impossible. (There is no figure with exactly one odd vertex; in fact, there is no figure with an odd number of odd vertices.)

In the Königsberg case, all four vertices have an odd

number of lines (bridges), therefore there is no solution and the people of Königsberg are wasting their time trying to take such a walk.

Euler's most important contribution to topology was not the solution of this puzzle, but his famous formula about the relationship between the number of vertices, edges, and faces of a polyhedron, which later became one of the central theorems of the subject. Take, as an example of a polyhedron, the room where you're sitting. The faces are the planes—the walls, ceiling, and floor. The edges are the lines where they meet—the corners of the room and the places around the ceiling and floor where the builders put moldings. The vertices are the points where the edges meet.

Euler's formula, which the SMSG text treats in the eighth grade, is:

$$V - E + F = 2$$

Count them for your own room and (if it is the usual shape) you will get: 8 vertices, 6 faces, and 12 edges. Substituting in the formula, $8 - 12 + 6$ does equal 2. It will if your room is octagonal or any other polyhedral shape, or even if you are in the Fun House with slanting floor and crazy walls. These are all simple polyhedrons—simple because there is no hole through them. In topology, a hole means something like the hole in a doughnut, which would correspond to a tunnel through your room. It does not mean a hole such as might be knocked in the wall.

Since this theorem does not depend on the areas of the faces or the lengths of the edges, but only concerns their number, it obviously has a topological nature. Descartes

observed the relationship a hundred years before Euler
did, but Euler proved it for all simple polyhedrons and it
carries his name.

Topology as a separate study got under way about the
middle of the nineteenth century with the discoveries of
Moebius, a German geometer, and others. The Moebius
strip is a surface with only one side. Most surfaces have
two—for instance, this page, which is printed on both its
sides. A bug, if he were prevented from crossing over the
edges, could never crawl from one side to the other.

To make a Moebius strip, unroll a length of paper—it
will show up better if the two sides are different colors—
give it a half twist, and scotch tape the ends together so
that you have a smooth continuous band, but with a twist
in it.

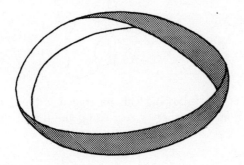

A bug crawling along the middle of the blue side will
soon be on the white side without ever crossing the edge.
Furthermore, there is only one edge. Trace it with your
finger and you see that it is a single closed curve. If you
had pasted the paper together without giving it a twist so

that you had an ordinary band, its edges would be two separate curves.

If you want to pick up a little money, bet somebody on what will happen if you cut the strip along a center line parallel to the edge. Most everybody will say that you will get two strips, but you don't. It makes a new Moebius strip, twice as long and half as wide. Now bet again on the outcome if you make another cut the same way as before on this second strip. This time you do get two separate strips, but intertwined.

### PROBLEMS

1. Which of the following are simple closed curves?

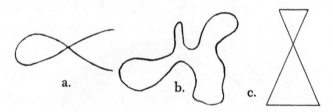

2. Which of the following can be traced without lifting the pencil from the paper or recrossing the line it makes?

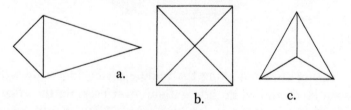

3. How many faces does a polyhedron have, if it has 12 vertices and 30 edges?

## OTHER NON-METRIC GEOMETRY

Topology is a non-metric geometry, because it has nothing to do with size, but there are also other kinds, some of which are presented in the seventh-grade text developed by the University of Maryland Mathematics Project, and also those of the School Mathematics Study Group for the seventh and eighth grades.

The criterion is whether the ideas of distance and measurement are introduced. In non-metric geometry, no line is said to be three inches long, no angle is specified as 45 degrees. The only numbers used are for counting sides, vertices, faces, etc.—not measuring them.

Non-metric geometry concerns space perception, either two- or three-dimensional. (Don't say solid geometry, say space geometry.) Nowadays, the concept of space is introduced as a set of points. Think of a swarm of immobilized flies filling your room. True, a fly is too fat to represent a point very well (since a point has no dimensions at all—only position) but so is the conventional pencil mark you make to represent a point on the plane of your paper. Picture an oversize sheet of cellophane stretched across the room—it divides it into two half spaces, the set of points on one side of the cellophane plane and the set of points on the other. The plane is not in either half space.

Out of the set of points in space, various subsets can be formed according to the conditions laid down in each case. The simplest subset in each category is called a simplex. The simplest of the simplexes is a set consisting of just one point. Since this single point has no length, width, or thickness, it is a 0-simplex.

A straight line segment is a 1-simplex, having only one dimension—length. If some of the flies drew themselves up in single file, they could represent a line segment, but you don't really need all of them. Any two are sufficient, since through any two different points in space there is exactly one straight line. In other words, a set of two points will determine a straight line.

A set of three points in space, if they are not all in the same straight line, will determine a triangle. With its interior, a triangle is the simplest plane figure—a 2-simplex, with two dimensions, length and width.

A set of four points in space, if they are not all in the same plane, determines a tetrahedron (a pyramid on a triangular base). A tetrahedron has four faces, each of which is a triangle. It is a three-dimensional figure, like all of us, with length, width, and height. From the non-metric point of view, it is the simplest and is called a 3-simplex.

These four simplexes—point, line segment, triangular region, and solid tetrahedron—are the building blocks out of which other figures are made. Any polyhedron is the union of a finite number of simplexes, whether it takes one or a million.

Another geometry of the non-metric kind is projective geometry. You can see that it is non-metric if you hold a pencil over a table with a light above it. The shadow, which is a sort of projection of the shape of the pencil, changes in length as you vary the angle at which you are holding the pencil. Stand it upright and the shadow is very short; hold it horizontally and the shadow is always larger than the size of the pencil. The measure of the length of the pencil, a metric property, is not preserved in its projected image, the shadow.

The SMSG program introduces some of the basic ideas of projective geometry in the eighth grade. The subject itself originated during the Renaissance with the invention of perspective drawing. In ancient times the relative size of figures in a painting was dictated by the subjects' social position. The king was always the largest, then the next most important person, and so on down to the—literally—little people.

During the fourteenth century, painters began to try for a realistic representation of a three-dimensional scene on their two-dimensional canvas, which they thought of as a transparent window looking onto the visible world beyond. In this concept, rays of light come from every point in the scene, intersect the canvas, and converge in the artist's eye. Every point in the picture matches a point in the object being painted.

To help fix these points correctly, mechanical devices were introduced. Among the first was a sighter, to squint through with one eye, and a glass plate held in a frame an arm's length away. The scene could then be outlined on the glass, exactly as it appeared, and afterward traced on the drawing.

A later apparatus, ascribed to Albrecht Dürer, the German painter, used a piece of string as a line of sight. It was pinned to a point on the object, run through an empty frame, and fastened to the eye of a needle driven into the wall. The position of the point where the string intersected the plane of the frame was fixed by two cross threads set in the frame at right angles to each other, like the grid on a piece of graph paper. As the string was pinned successively to key points in the still life, the other end remained fixed to the eye of the needle, so that all the lines converged there, instead of in the artist's eye, leaving him free to move around.

However, no mechanical device could take the place of a knowledge of the mathematical principles involved in this projection of a real scene onto a canvas plane. As Dürer himself wrote, "Geometry is the right foundation of all painting." (This was before the advent of abstract expressionism.) He also understood that perspective was an important branch of mathematics, not just a technique of drawing.

The originator of projective geometry, as such, was a seventeenth-century architect and engineer, Gerard Desargues. He wrote a book, intended to help artists, which contained the ideas of geometry that are useful in a study of perspective.

A noticeable difference between Euclidean and projective geometry is in their treatment of parallels. In Euclidean geometry parallel lines never meet—they have no point in common. In projective geometry they do. They intersect in what is called an ideal point (similar to the vanishing point in perspective drawing). The set of all points on a line is made up of all the real points, plus an ideal point.

Actually, this is just a change in language. "Two lines are parallel," and "Two lines intersect in an ideal point," say the same thing in different words. It is not meant to imply that the lines *really* meet in a point way off yonder, any more than the railroad tracks do. This mathematical convention is adopted so that in projective geometry you can say any two lines in a plane meet in a point of some sort. Furthermore, all these ideal points lie on the same line—the ideal line. (Think of the horizon, or eye level, line in perspective drawing.)

These geometries are alike in that both are the study of properties which remain invariant under transformation. (So is topology.) The difference is in the kind of transformation. In Euclidean geometry it is rigid motion that moves the figures from place to place without changing their size or shape. Size is a metric property; therefore the geometry of Euclid is a metric geometry.

Projection changes both size and shape. The properties that remain invariant are something else. For instance, the projection of a triangle is always a triangle of some sort and that of a quadrilateral is always a quadrilateral. A square may become a trapezoid or some other four-sided figure, but it will remain four-sided, and the projection of a straight line is never curved.

In topology, the transformations are much more drastic. Triangles may become circles, squares may be remolded into decagons. No property of either size, shape, or number of sides is invariant, but a simple closed curve is always a simple closed curve, with one inside and one outside.

## Problems

Solve each of the following problems and classify it as metric or non-metric:

1. A 2-simplex is the union of how many 1-simplexes?
2. A 3-simplex has how many 2-simplexes as faces?

3. Find the volume of a rectangular solid 5 feet long, 4 feet wide, and 2½ feet high.
4. What kind of line—real or ideal—is determined by each of the following sets of points?
   a. 2 real points
   b. 1 real point and 1 ideal point
   c. 2 ideal points
5. What is the area of an equilateral triangle whose side is 3 feet?

## CLASSICAL GEOMETRY

If you have a child in the tenth grade, he is probably taking geometry. This is the traditional Euclidean variety —there are no figures drawn on silly putty and stretched out of shape. Nevertheless, there have been changes.

The first thing you are likely to notice if you look at the text is that plane and solid geometry have been fused into one course in, roughly, the ratio of 5 to 1. How is it possible to cover all this in one year, when it used to take a year and a half? To begin with, the number of theorems of plane geometry which are proved has been drastically cut, following the recommendation of the Commission on Mathematics of the College Entrance Examination Board. (The old books had over a hundred—the new ones usually have less than fifty.) Their reasons are that, while it is essential for the students to learn the nature of deductive reasoning and the meaning of formal proof, a short chain of theorems will accomplish this end as well as a long one, and the time is better spent in original thinking and discovery—i.e., problem-solving.

Everybody knows a girl who got through geometry by

simply memorizing the words of the proofs. She knew that step five said angle $A$ was equal to angle $B$ because the base angles of an isosceles triangle are equal. To her, this had absolutely no connection with the figure—she could rattle it off just as fluently without one. In fact, you only confused her if you constructed an isosceles triangle and lettered it $XYZ$. She's going to have a harder time with the new course, because there is more thinking and less memorizing.

Solid geometry itself has been cut to the bone. The commission felt that what the students need is the ability to handle problems involving space relationships. This calls for facility in visualizing three-dimensional figures and knowledge of the facts about lines, planes, angles, and solids (including formulas for areas and volumes). Few, if any, of these theorems are proved formally. Often topics in solid geometry are introduced right after corresponding topics in plane geometry. For instance, the study of a line tangent to a circle is followed by the analogous proposition in three dimensions of a plane tangent to a sphere.

The second major change you are apt to notice is that there is some algebra in the geometry book. This in in line with the over-all trend toward less compartmentalization of learning. The College Board's Commission on Mathematics, as well as other groups, opposed the artificial isolation of geometry in the curriculum. Under the former program, it was usually taught in between two years of algebra, but divorced from them.

Algebra gained admission into the geometry course through the commission's recommendation that analytic proofs for some theorems be accepted, as well as the traditional synthetic ones. (These terms have special mathematical meanings that you would not guess from the words. "Synthetic" is not meant to imply anything ersatz, but is the name given to the classical method of Euclid, in which the subject is built upon purely geometrical foundations without the use of algebra, since in his time, there wasn't any. "Analytic" proofs use algebra and the system of coordinates invented by Descartes.) An analytic proof is often shorter and simpler than the corresponding synthetic one for the same theorem, as you can see from these two contrasting methods of proving "A line segment joining the midpoints of two sides of a triangle is equal to one-half the third side":

Analytic:

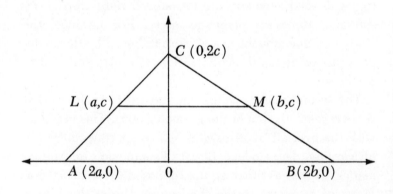

Given: Triangle $ABC$, with vertices $A(2a,0)$, $B(2b,0)$, and $C(0,2c)$.

L and M the midpoints of AC and BC, respectively

To prove: $LM = \frac{1}{2}AB$

Proof: The coordinates of $L$ are $\dfrac{2a + 0}{2}$, or $a$, and $\dfrac{0 + 2c}{2}$, or $c$

The coordinates of $M$ are $\dfrac{2b + 0}{2}$, or $b$, and $\dfrac{0 + 2c}{2}$, or $c$

$$LM = \sqrt{(b - a)^2 + (c - c)^2} = \sqrt{(b - a)^2 + 0}$$
$$= \sqrt{(b - a)^2}$$
$$= b - a$$
$$AB = \sqrt{(2b - 2a)^2 + (0 - 0)^2} = \sqrt{(2b - 2a)^2}$$
$$= 2b - 2a \text{ or } 2(b - a)$$

Therefore $LM = \frac{1}{2}AB$

($2a$, $2b$, and $2c$ are used instead of $a$, $b$, and $c$ to avoid fractions and make the algebra easier.)

Synthetic:

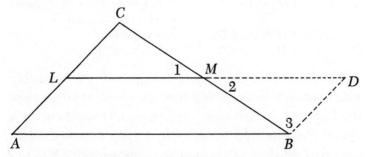

Given: Triangle $ABC$

       $L$ and $M$ the midpoints of $AC$ and $BC$, respectively

To prove: $LM = \frac{1}{2}AB$

Proof:

Extend $LM$ its own length to $D$. Draw $DB$.

| | |
|---|---|
| Angle 1 = Angle 2 | Vertical angles are equal |
| $CM = MB$ | Definition of midpoint |
| $LM = MD$ | Construction |
| Triangle $CLM$ = Triangle $MBD$ | Side Angle Side |
| Angle 3 = Angle $C$ | Corresponding parts of congruent triangles are equal |
| $AC \parallel BD$ | Lines are parallel if alternate interior angles are equal |
| $CL = BD$ | Corresponding parts of congruent triangles are equal |
| $CL = AL$ | Definition of midpoint |
| $BD = AL$ | Substitution ($BD$ for $CL$) |
| $ABDL$ is a parallelogram | A quadrilateral is a parallelogram if a pair of opposite sides is both equal and parallel |
| $LD = AB$ | Opposite sides of a parallelogram are equal |
| $LM = \frac{1}{2}\ LD$ | Bisection |
| $LM = \frac{1}{2}\ AB$ | Substitution |

The third change is more subtle and you probably won't notice it in thumbing through a text. It stems from the fact that we are now, mathematically speaking, in a period characterized by devotion to precision and rigorous proof. Modern mathematicians, in their pursuit of unimpeachable logic, now fault even the former master and speak of the repair work necessary on Euclidean geometry, once considered the cathedral of logical rigor.

*106*
*21*

Strictly speaking, this is new only by comparison with Euclid's two thousand years, since David Hilbert's *Foundations of Geometry* was published in 1899. What *is* new is that the results of this remodeling have now trickled down to the high school level.

The logical defects in Euclid's structure—pointed out in background reading, not in the texts—include these:

1. He has no postulate for order, that is, no way of proving that $P$ is between, or not between, $A$ and $B$. This leads to paradoxes.

2. He failed to see that a logical treatment of any branch of mathematics must start with undefined terms. He attempted to define everything, including "point" and "line."

3. He has a postulate setting down the conditions under which two *straight* lines will intersect, but he lacks a similar one for circles. Many geometric figures are constructed with the compasses by first cutting two arcs and then using their intersection to fix a desired point. Euclid just tacitly assumed they would intersect. The organization of a deductive system requires that all other statements of the system must be deducible from the initial ones. If any additional assumptions creep into the work, they are considered to be blemishes. If you take the point of view that *all* you know about circles must come from the postulates, then you would not *know* the conditions under which they will always intersect.

# *Matrices* 8

You can't be *au courant* with the new mathematics without knowing what a matrix is. The term means a rectangular array of entries (usually numerals) lined up in rows and columns, such as:

$$\begin{pmatrix} 5 & 1 & 2 \\ 1 & 4 & 0 \\ 6 & 3 & 4 \end{pmatrix}$$

This is a square matrix, 3 by 3, but any rectangular arrangement is possible. You can have 2 by 3 matrices, 1 by 4 matrices, 4 by 2 matrices, and so on. (The number of rows is always written first and then the number of columns.) Here is a 2 by 3 matrix:

$$\begin{pmatrix} 1 & 6 & 5 \\ 2 & 3 & 4 \end{pmatrix}$$

A 3 by 2 would look like this:

$$\begin{pmatrix} 0 & 1 \\ 7 & 4 \\ 2 & 5 \end{pmatrix}$$

The idea of arranging objects in a rectangular pattern is very simple and examples abound—stars in the flag (before Alaska and Hawaii), sheets of trading stamps, eggs in a carton. Arrays of dots, crosses, circles, and the like,

are used in the SMSG text for the fourth grade to teach
multiplication, because an array gives a picture of a mathematical sentence. $2 \times 3 = 6$ could be illustrated by:

```
o   o   o

o   o   o
```

This 2 by 3 array can be turned to form a 3 by 2 array for
the sentence $3 \times 2 = 6$:

```
o   o

o   o

o   o
```

Since the total number of dots is obviously not changed
merely by turning the configuration around, here is a clear
demonstration of the commutative property of multiplication—i.e., $2 \times 3 = 3 \times 2$ (see Chapter V).

Children may discover the multiplication facts by
means of arrays. (Discover is a big word in all the new
texts, since the trend in modern mathematics is toward
more understanding and less memorizing by rote.) Arrays, then, help the children DISCOVER new multiplication
facts from the ones they already know. For instance, this
large 6 by 14 array can be separated into two smaller
arrays—a 6 by 10 and a 6 by 4.

```
.   .   .   .   .   .   .   .   .   .  |  .   .   .   .

.   .   .   .   .   .   .   .   .   .  |  .   .   .   .

.   .   .   .   .   .   .   .   .   .  |  .   .   .   .

.   .   .   .   .   .   .   .   .   .  |  .   .   .   .

.   .   .   .   .   .   .   .   .   .  |  .   .   .   .

.   .   .   .   .   .   .   .   .   .  |  .   .   .   .
```

Since the product of 6 × 10 has been learned previously, and also the product of 6 × 4, all Billy has to do is add 60 and 24 to arrive at 84, the product of 6 × 14. Think of each array as an entity—don't count all those dots, but look for familiar arrays within unknown ones. Of course, there are others in the problem above which could just as well have been used as the ones we chose. 6 by 8 and 6 by 6 would work, or two 6 by 7's, or any combination where the second factors in each pair add up to 14.

An array of dots is a sort of forerunner of a matrix. It is also tied in with the set concept. The chart above could represent all the possible matchings of the 6 members of one set with the 14 members of the other set. Each dot stands for an ordered pair (see Chapter II).

Matrices themselves provide a very powerful condensed language in which complicated mathematical statements can be expressed simply. Computations for rocket and projectile flight use matrices. They are an indispensable tool in atomic physics, electrical engineering, statistics, and modern economic theory. A great number of the operations performed by giant computers involve matrices.

## OPERATIONS WITH MATRICES

Although matrix algebra is close to the frontiers of mathematics, the Madison Project presents a junior version to sixth-graders. The SMSG has a higher-level course for seniors in high school.

The first thing to understand when working with matrices is that a change in the position of the entries makes a difference. These two matrices are not the same, even though they contain the same numbers.

$$\begin{pmatrix} 1 & 3 \\ 2 & 4 \end{pmatrix} \qquad \begin{pmatrix} 3 & 1 \\ 2 & 4 \end{pmatrix}$$

Two matrices are equal only if each entry in one is equal to the corresponding entry in the other. The two examples above are not equal, but these are:

$$\begin{pmatrix} 1 & 3 \\ 2 & 4 \end{pmatrix} = \begin{pmatrix} \frac{4}{4} & \sqrt{9} \\ \frac{6}{3} & 2 \times 2 \end{pmatrix}$$

Furthermore, matrices, to be equal, must have the same dimensions. A 2 by 2 matrix cannot equal a 2 by 3 matrix, even if it is filled in with zeros.

$$\begin{pmatrix} 1 & 3 \\ 2 & 4 \end{pmatrix} \text{ does not equal } \begin{pmatrix} 1 & 3 & 0 \\ 2 & 4 & 0 \end{pmatrix}$$

Addition is performed exactly the way you would expect. Add each number in one matrix to its mate at the corresponding position in the other matrix and write the sum in that same position in the answer.

$$\begin{pmatrix} 1 & 3 \\ 2 & 4 \end{pmatrix} + \begin{pmatrix} 2 & 4 \\ 6 & 1 \end{pmatrix} = \begin{pmatrix} 3 & 7 \\ 8 & 5 \end{pmatrix}$$

Only matrices with like dimensions can be added.

$$\begin{pmatrix} 1 & 3 \\ 2 & 4 \end{pmatrix} + \begin{pmatrix} 2 & 4 \\ 6 & 1 \\ 0 & 0 \end{pmatrix} \text{ does not equal } \begin{pmatrix} 3 & 7 \\ 8 & 5 \\ 0 & 0 \end{pmatrix}$$

These two matrices cannot be added at all, since one is a 2 by 2 and the other a 3 by 2. Similarly, (0)—a 1 by 1 matrix—cannot be added to a matrix with different dimensions.

$$\begin{pmatrix} 1 & 3 \\ 2 & 4 \end{pmatrix} + (0) \text{ does not equal } \begin{pmatrix} 1 & 3 \\ 2 & 4 \end{pmatrix}$$

If you are looking for the identity element for addition —a matrix that behaves the way 0 does in ordinary addition—it has to be a matrix made up of zeros, but having the same dimensions as the matrix you wish to add it to.

$$\begin{pmatrix} 1 & 3 \\ 2 & 4 \end{pmatrix} + \begin{pmatrix} 0 & 0 \\ 0 & 0 \end{pmatrix} = \begin{pmatrix} 1 & 3 \\ 2 & 4 \end{pmatrix}$$

Adding a matrix to itself, as in this example:

$$\begin{pmatrix} 3 & 1 \\ 5 & 6 \end{pmatrix} + \begin{pmatrix} 3 & 1 \\ 5 & 6 \end{pmatrix} = \begin{pmatrix} 6 & 2 \\ 10 & 12 \end{pmatrix}$$

could be written more compactly as:

$$2 \begin{pmatrix} 3 & 1 \\ 5 & 6 \end{pmatrix} = \begin{pmatrix} 6 & 2 \\ 10 & 12 \end{pmatrix}$$

Here 2 is a number and is written without parentheses, to show that it is not a 1 by 1 matrix. Multiplication of a matrix by a number (called a scalar) turns out just as you probably would predict. It simply multiplies every entry in the matrix by that number.

Multiplication of a matrix by a matrix is considerably more complicated. If you guessed that you merely multiply each pair of corresponding entries together, you are wrong.

The Madison Project's book *Matrices, Functions, and Other Topics* explains it to sixth-graders as "candy store arithmetic" and illustrates the process with a story about a boy who bought three almond bars, four peppermints, and zero boxes of chocolate-covered ants (a very wise distribution of his money, if you ask me).

Without the candy, it works like this: Take each entry in a *row* of the first matrix and multiply it by the corresponding entry in a fixed *column* of the second matrix. In other words—first row, second entry times first column, second entry. So far, in the problem

$\begin{pmatrix} 3 & 1 \\ 5 & 6 \end{pmatrix} \times \begin{pmatrix} 4 & 2 \\ 7 & 8 \end{pmatrix}$ you have $3 \times 4 = 12$, and $1 \times 7 = 7$.

Add these two products ($12 + 7 = 19$) and write the sum in the first row, first column of your answer.

$$\begin{pmatrix} 19 & - \\ - & - \end{pmatrix}$$

Now do the same thing for the first row of the first matrix and the *second* column of the second matrix. $3 \times 2 = 6$, and $1 \times 8 = 8$. Add these two products ($6 + 8 = 14$) and fill in the proper spot in your answer.

$$\begin{pmatrix} 19 & 14 \\ - & - \end{pmatrix}$$

Repeat the procedure with the second row of the first matrix and the first column of the other matrix. $5 \times 4 = 20$, and $6 \times 7 = 42$. Take the sum ($20 + 42 = 62$) and write it in where it belongs.

$$\begin{pmatrix} 19 & 14 \\ 62 & - \end{pmatrix}$$

Finish up with $5 \times 2 = 10$, and $6 \times 8 = 48$. Add 10 and 48 and write 58 in your answer.

$$\begin{pmatrix} 19 & 14 \\ 62 & 58 \end{pmatrix}$$

The two matrices in this problem are both 2 by 2's. Can matrices with different dimensions be multiplied, or—like addition—do they have to be alike? The answer is that they have to partially match. The number of columns of the first must be the same as the number of rows of the second. For instance, you can multiply a 1 by 3 matrix by a 3 by 1 matrix, such as this:

$$(5 \quad 1 \quad 2) \times \begin{pmatrix} 0 \\ 4 \\ 1 \end{pmatrix} = (6)$$

First row, first column $(5 \times 0) + (1 \times 4) + (2 \times 1) =$
$$0 \quad + \quad 4 \quad + \quad 2 \quad = 6.$$
But you couldn't take a 1 by 3 times a 2 by 1.

$$(5 \quad 1 \quad 2) \times \begin{pmatrix} 0 \\ 4 \end{pmatrix}$$

If you try, you get: first row, first column $(5 \times 0) + (1 \times 4) + (2 \times -)$. You see that there is nothing to multiply the 2—the last entry of the row—by. Therefore, multiplication is impossible in such a case.

If you study the structure of matrix algebra as a mathematical system (see Chapter V), the question of identity elements for addition and multiplication comes up. We found the additive identity, or zero matrix, a few pages back, but is there a matrix that plays the same role as 1 in ordinary multiplication? A logical guess would be a matrix in which every entry is 1, but if you try an example you see it doesn't work.

$$\begin{pmatrix} 1 & 2 \\ 3 & 4 \end{pmatrix} \times \begin{pmatrix} 1 & 1 \\ 1 & 1 \end{pmatrix} = \begin{pmatrix} 3 & 3 \\ 7 & 7 \end{pmatrix}$$

First row, first column $(1 \times 1) + (2 \times 1) =$
$$1 + 2 = 3$$
First row, second column $(1 \times 1) + (2 \times 1) =$
$$1 + 2 = 3$$
Second row, first column $(3 \times 1) + (4 \times 1) =$
$$3 + 4 = 7$$
Second row, second column $(3 \times 1) + (4 \times 1) =$
$$3 + 4 = 7$$

The answer is certainly not identical with the first matrix.

The Madison Project has a film showing fifth- and sixth-graders having a lesson on matrices. These children are also trying to discover the special matrix that acts like 1. They, too, guess wrong before hitting on the right one, which you see below.

$$\begin{pmatrix} 1 & 2 \\ 3 & 4 \end{pmatrix} \times \begin{pmatrix} 1 & 0 \\ 0 & 1 \end{pmatrix} = \begin{pmatrix} 1 & 2 \\ 3 & 4 \end{pmatrix}$$

First row, first column $(1 \times 1) + (2 \times 0) = 1$
First row, second column $(1 \times 0) + (2 \times 1) =$
$$0 + 2 = 2$$
Second row, first column $(3 \times 1) + (4 \times 0) =$
$$3 + 0 = 3$$
Second row, second column $(3 \times 0) + (4 \times 1) =$
$$0 + 4 = 4$$

Another question in the study of the structure of matrix algebra is: Does its multiplication obey the law of commutation? (See Chapter V). Is Matrix *A* times Matrix *B* the same as Matrix *B* times Matrix *A*? Go back to the first problem we did in matrix multiplication, which was:

$$\begin{pmatrix} 3 & 1 \\ 5 & 6 \end{pmatrix} \times \begin{pmatrix} 4 & 2 \\ 7 & 8 \end{pmatrix} = \begin{pmatrix} 19 & 14 \\ 62 & 58 \end{pmatrix}$$

Now try it reversed and you, too, may DISCOVER something.

$$\begin{pmatrix} 4 & 2 \\ 7 & 8 \end{pmatrix} \times \begin{pmatrix} 3 & 1 \\ 5 & 6 \end{pmatrix}$$

First row, first column $(4 \times 3) + (2 \times 5) =$
$$12 + 10 = 22$$
First row, second column $(4 \times 1) + (2 \times 6) =$
$$4 + 12 = 16$$
Second row, first column $(7 \times 3) + (8 \times 5) =$
$$21 + 40 = 61$$
Second row, second column $(7 \times 1) + (8 \times 6) =$
$$7 + 48 = 55$$

Did you get the same answer you did the first time? I didn't. I got:

$$\begin{pmatrix} 4 & 2 \\ 7 & 8 \end{pmatrix} \times \begin{pmatrix} 3 & 1 \\ 5 & 6 \end{pmatrix} = \begin{pmatrix} 22 & 16 \\ 61 & 55 \end{pmatrix}$$

Therefore, matrix multiplication, unlike multiplication in ordinary arithmetic, is not a commutative operation.

### PROBLEMS

1. Find the value of $x$ and $y$:

$$\begin{pmatrix} 1 & 2 & 3 \\ 4 & 6 & 7 \\ 5 & 8 & 9 \end{pmatrix} = \begin{pmatrix} 1 & 2 & y/3 \\ 2x & 6 & 7 \\ 5 & 8 & 9 \end{pmatrix}$$

Perform the following computations, where possible:

2. $\begin{pmatrix} 1 & 7 \\ 5 & 2 \end{pmatrix} + \begin{pmatrix} 3 & 6 \\ 1 & 4 \end{pmatrix}$

3. $2 \times \begin{pmatrix} 6 & 3 \\ 5 & 4 \end{pmatrix}$

4. $\begin{pmatrix} 4 & 2 & 5 \\ 6 & 3 & 0 \end{pmatrix} + \begin{pmatrix} 2 & -3 \\ 5 & 7 \\ 0 & -1 \end{pmatrix}$

5. $\begin{pmatrix} 1 & 8 \\ 5 & 2 \end{pmatrix} \times \begin{pmatrix} 3 & 4 \\ 10 & 0 \end{pmatrix}$

6. $3\begin{pmatrix} -6 & 0 \\ 5 & 1 \end{pmatrix} + 2\begin{pmatrix} -4 & 1 \\ -8 & 0 \end{pmatrix}$

7. $\begin{pmatrix} 6 & 5 & 2 \end{pmatrix} \times \begin{pmatrix} -4 & 0 & 5 \\ 3 & 2 & 1 \end{pmatrix}$

8. $\begin{pmatrix} -5 \\ 2 \\ 1 \end{pmatrix} \times \begin{pmatrix} 1 & 6 & -8 \end{pmatrix}$

9. $\begin{pmatrix} 5 & 11 \\ 12 & 8 \end{pmatrix} \times \begin{pmatrix} 1 & 0 \\ 0 & 1 \end{pmatrix}$

10. If these two matrices are multiplied, what will be the number at the intersection of the second row and third column of the answer?

$$\begin{pmatrix} 3 & 6 & 0 \\ -1 & 5 & 8 \\ -7 & 0 & 2 \end{pmatrix} \times \begin{pmatrix} 1 & 7 & 4 \\ -2 & 3 & 1 \\ 5 & 4 & 6 \end{pmatrix}$$

# Probability 9

Flip a nickel and who can tell whether it will come up heads or tails? Flip a truckload of nickels and, almost surely, they will come up close to half and half. In physics this principle is widely used to study the constant, violent, and *random* motion of molecules. No one can predict where any one molecule will go, and no one cares, but the action of millions of molecules can be foretold rather closely, like that of the nickels.

Small particles suspended in liquid or gas are kicked around by the molecules' movement. A photographic representation of the erratic, zigzag path of one of these particles looks very much like the drawing for a random walk problem in a mathematics text on probability.

In politics, the public opinion poll can make or break. Governor Rockefeller gave his ratings on these polls as his reason for not seeking the presidential nomination in 1960. Opinion research is a fast-growing science that talks in millions, and yet how many people do you know who have actually been polled? The researchers base their reports on interviews with a random sample, selected by probability mathematics.

Just taking a large number of people for the sample will not do the trick, as some have learned the hard way. The classic example is the old *Literary Digest* poll in the presidential election of 1936. The poll "elected" Landon but the voters elected Roosevelt, and by a landslide. How could they be so wrong? Ph.D. theses have been written on the *Digest's* errors, the consensus being that the sample was badly biased. The magazine picked their millions of names from telephone books, lists of automobile owners, and their own subscribers. In the depression year of '36, this was hardly a representative cross section of the population. As everybody knows, the *Literary Digest* folded after their fiasco. Today's pollsters use scientific sampling, with specialists in probability mathematics to reduce the margins of error.

Probability—defined as the study of phenomena in which chance plays a role—became a branch of mathematics in the seventeenth century when a dice player, the Chevalier de Méré, wrote to his friend asking for the proper odds on throwing at least one 12 out of 24 tosses of a pair of dice. He made a good choice of friends, because it was Blaise Pascal, one of the foremost mathematicians in France, that he sent his question to. Pascal became interested in studying the problem, and corresponded with Fermat about it. Fermat, although his profession was the law, was a major figure in several fields of mathematics, and out of the work of these two men came much of the theory of probability.

(If you want to know the answer to the dice player's problem, the odds, roughly, are 229 to 220 against throwing a 12—a losing bet at even money, as De Méré had already found out.)

Since the subject that began with the study of gambling

has burgeoned to include problems in economics, sociology, heredity, politics, and physics, the rudiments of probability are now taught in the elementary grades. Children draw colored marbles from a bag, spin pointers, pick numbered slips from a hat, and roll cubical blocks marked with letters or numerals on the sides. These activities are sprinkled into the arithmetic lessons to familiarize them with the fundamental, intuitive ideas of probability and the language of chance.

The text *Mathematics for the Junior High School, Second Book* (Eighth Grade) developed by the University of Maryland Mathematics Project introduces more extensive calculation of the probability of events, and the SMSG texts include it in both seventh and eighth grades. There are commercially prepared kits available with materials for laboratory experiments in probability.

The Commission on Mathematics of the College Board thought so highly of the subject that they wrote a text, *Introductory Probability and Statistical Inference*, to be used in an experimental course for seniors in high school. Some schools offer this one semester and the SMSG course on matrix algebra (see Chapter VIII) the other. More often, the study of probability is incorporated in other courses.

## SIMPLE PROBABILITY

Mathematically, the probability of an event's happening is expressed as a fraction somewhere between 1 (a dead certainty) and 0 (no chance at all). The numerator of the fraction is the number of ways it *could* happen, the

denominator is the total number of possible outcomes—
both happening and failing to happen. If you flip a coin,
the probability of heads is ½—out of the two ways it can
land, heads or tails, there is one possibility of its being a
head.

The Ginn Arithmetic Enrichment Program's text for the
fifth grade introduces probability as an application of
fractions and ratios. One meaning of the fraction ½ is one
out of two or the ratio of one to two.

If you draw a card from a full deck, the probability of
getting a heart is $\frac{13}{52}$, because out of 52 cards there are
13 hearts. The probability of drawing a king—any king—is
$\frac{4}{52}$. The probability of your card's being the king of
hearts is $\frac{1}{52}$. There is only one king of hearts in the entire deck, therefore only one possible way in which that
event could happen.

This is not the same as the odds. They express the ratio
of the possibility of an event's happening to the possibility
of its failing to happen. The odds on drawing a heart are
13 to 39. Out of the 52 cards, there are 13 chances of getting a heart and 39 chances of getting something else—a
non-heart, in other words.

The *probability* of a non-heart is $\frac{39}{52}$. Add this to the
probability of drawing a heart—$\frac{13}{52}$—and it comes out
$\frac{52}{52}$, or 1. The total of all the probabilities of all the
possible outcomes of a single trial of an experiment is always 1, and you can use that fact to check your problems.
In this case there are just two possibilities—heart or non-
heart—so the card is certain to be one or the other, and a
probability of 1 expresses a certainty.

Probabilities are most easily understood in terms of

sets. If set *A* consists of all the hearts in the deck, then the set of all non-hearts is the complement of *A* (see Chapter II). Together they make up the universal set. In Venn diagrams it looks like this, with the rectangle representing the entire deck of cards:

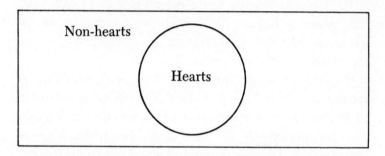

There are two widely held misconceptions about events that depend on luck. One is the theory of the maturation of the chances, usually called the law of averages. If you are flipping a coin and heads comes up a number of times in succession, many people say: "By the law of averages, the next toss is more likely to be tails." It is not. The probability of tails is exactly the same as it was in the first place—one-half. The fallacy comes in applying to the total of a series, part of which is already known, the formula of probability, which is designed only for the unknown future. If you are performing the experiment of tossing a coin (known to be perfect) twenty times and the first eight trials have already turned out to be heads, the best prediction of the outcome is that the remaining twelve tosses will most likely be half and half, giving a total of fourteen heads and six tails.

The other misconception is the opposite—a belief in

streaks of luck. The dice are hot, they say, or he's holding a hot hand. These people think that, after a succession of heads, the next toss is *more* likely to be heads. They, also, are wrong. The probability of an event's occurring is still the same, regardless of what happened before—provided, of course, that the coin is perfect, the dice are true, and the deck is not stacked.

## PROBLEMS

1. The days of the week are each written on a separate slip and put in a box. If you draw one without looking, what is the probability of getting Tuesday?

2. A bag contains a number of Christmas balls—all either red or green—and you take one out, blindfolded. If the probability of getting a red one is known to be $\frac{5}{11}$, what is the probability of a green one?

3. In your pocket you have 2 dimes, 1 quarter, 3 nickels, and a fifty-cent piece. If you reach in and take a coin at random, what is the probability it will be a dime? What is the probability that it will not be a silver coin?

4. If a single die is rolled, what is the probability that it stops with an even number showing on the top face?

5. A box contains a dozen pieces of fruit—seven apples and five pears. If you take one at random, what are the odds that it will be an apple? What is the probability it will be an apple?

## COMPOUND PROBABILITY

Suppose you are interested in the outcome of two chance events which are independent of each other. Say you roll two dice—what is the probability that one will come to rest showing a 5 on the top face and the other will also come up 5? It is easy to figure the probability of each event separately—out of the six numerals on a single die there is only one 5, so the probability of getting a 5 on one die is ⅙. Since the conditions of the problem will be met only if there is a 5 on one die *and* a 5 on the other also, you might be tempted to add the two probabilities, but that will not work.

To analyze the situation, think of one red die and one white die and make a chart called the "sample space" of all the ways each number on the red die could be paired with each number on the white die. Always naming the red die first, you would have:

$$(1,1) \quad (1,2) \quad (1,3) \quad (1,4) \quad (1,5) \quad (1,6)$$
$$(2,1) \quad (2,2) \quad (2,3) \quad (2,4) \quad (2,5) \quad (2,6)$$
$$(3,1) \quad (3,2) \quad (3,3) \quad (3,4) \quad (3,5) \quad (3,6)$$
$$(4,1) \quad (4,2) \quad (4,3) \quad (4,4) \quad (4,5) \quad (4,6)$$
$$(5,1) \quad (5,2) \quad (5,3) \quad (5,4) \quad (5,5) \quad (5,6)$$
$$(6,1) \quad (6,2) \quad (6,3) \quad (6,4) \quad (6,5) \quad (6,6)$$

These are exactly the members of the Cartesian product of the set of six numbers shown on the red die and set of six numbers shown on the white die (see Chapter II). There are 36 ordered pairs in this sample space and only one of them (5,5) is the one we want. Therefore the probability of both dice coming up 5 is ⅟₃₆.

You see that adding ⅙ and ⅙ will not make ⅟₃₆, but multiplying them will. The rule is: To find the probability that a number of independent events will all occur simultaneously, multiply together the separate probabilities of each of them. For example, suppose you flip a coin, draw a card from a full deck, and roll a die. What is the probability that you see a head on the coin, a queen on the card, and a 3 on the die? The probability of a head is ½, of a queen is $\frac{4}{52}$, and of a 3 on the die is $\frac{1}{6}$. $\frac{1}{2} \times \frac{4}{52} \times \frac{1}{6} = \frac{1}{156}$, much less than any one of them separately. Had you added you would have gotten a number larger than any of the individual probabilities, which is against common sense.

The National Aeronautics and Space Administration used this principle of multiplying probabilities in deciding which of three possible methods for making a manned moon expedition offered the best chance of success. They broke each of the choices—(A) Direct Approach, (B) Earth Orbit Rendezvous, (C) Lunar Orbit Rendezvous—down into major elements, from take-off to return. The probability of each element's success was determined, as far as possible, from previous performance. Then all these for method A were multiplied, giving the probability of successful completion of a moon shot by direct approach. B and C were computed in the same way, and from a comparison of the three, the lunar orbit rendezvous was selected as the most feasible. Here a decision of major importance was reached through the use of probability mathematics.

Often the problems call for the probability of one event *or* another. For example, suppose you win if one roll of a single die comes up 2 *or* 3. These are mutually exclusive events, since you can't get both a 2 and a 3 on one roll. In set language, the two sets are disjoint and a Venn diagram would look like this (see Chapter II):

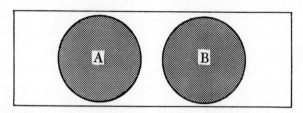

Clearly you have a better chance of winning on a proposition of this kind than on a bet specifying a single number. To find the probability you add the probability of getting a 2, which you already know is ⅙, to the probability of getting a 3, also ⅙, and you find the probability of winning is ²⁄₆. Incidentally, it is frequently better not to reduce these fractions to lowest terms, although it would not be wrong to say ⅓. The probabilities are easier to compare and handle if left with a denominator which is the total number of possibilities in the sample space. In the case of a single die, this is six.

Not all problems of this type are mutually exclusive, however. Suppose you flip a quarter and then draw a card from a full deck. What is the probability that you see a face on the quarter *or* on the card? There is no reason why you can't do both. Bear in mind that in probability "or" usually means "and/or." The two sets are *not* disjoint and a Venn diagram will show them overlapping.

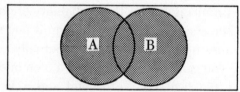

If you add the probability of seeing a face on the coin —½—to the probability of drawing a face card—$^{12}\!\!/_{52}$

(I am not including the aces)—you will get too high a number because you are counting the place where the two sets overlap twice. To keep from doing this, you have to subtract from the sum the probability of the joint occurrence. It is, of course, the probability associated with the intersection of the two sets which you found above by multiplying. Here it would be $\frac{1}{2} \times \frac{12}{52}$, which works out to be $\frac{6}{52}$.

The solution to the whole problem is: $\frac{1}{2} + \frac{12}{52} - \frac{6}{52} = \frac{32}{52}$.

### PROBLEMS

1. A box contains four red balls, three blue balls, two yellow balls, and one white ball. If you draw one ball, blindfolded, what is the probability that it will be either red or yellow?

2. If you draw one ball from the box in Problem 1, replace it, and draw again, what is the probability that both balls will be red?

3. If Tom draws a card from a full deck, and simultaneously, Bill draws a card from another full deck, what is the probability that Tom or Bill draws a heart?

4. In one roll of a pair of dice, what is the probability both dice will come to rest showing threes on the top faces?

5. In one roll of a pair of dice, what is the probability the sum of the numbers thrown will be six?

### BINOMIAL EXPERIMENTS

Having discussed gambling, we now turn to sex. In a family of three children, what is the probability that two are boys and one is a girl? This is called a binomial experiment because the results fall into one of just two categories—boys or girls. If you call $b$ the probability that a baby will be a boy and $g$ the probability of a girl, then the problem can be set up as $(b + g)^3$. The exponent is 3 because we specified that this was a family of three children. Had we said four children, the problem would become $(b + g)^4$.

To work the formula out, you have to brush up on the binomial theorem a little. Of course, you *could* just multiply $(b + g)$ by $(b + g)$ and then take that answer times $(b + g)$ again, but this is extremely long and tedious in problems involving families of eight or ten children. The binomial theorem provides a short cut, as follows.

In the expansion of $(b + g)^3$ the letters and their exponents are easily predictable. Leaving blanks for the coefficients, which we haven't worked out yet, $(b + g)^3$ = ___$b^3$ + ___$b^2g$ + ___$bg^2$ + ___$g^3$, as you can see by multiplying it out the long way, if you want to. The exponent of the first letter is 3, the power to which we are raising the binomial. Then in each succeeding term, that letter's exponent decreases by one. The second letter's exponents are similar, but in ascending order.

To fill in the blanks with the proper coefficients, follow Pascal's Triangle. This device, attributed to Blaise Pascal and probably used by him in De Méré's dice problem, is a sort of pyramid of numbers, following this pattern.

```
      1
      1  1
      1  2  1
      1  3  3  1
      1  4  6  4  1
      1  5  10  10  5  1
```

Working from the top down, the triangle can be extended as far as needed, as you can see in any second-year algebra book.

Since each row begins with 1, that doesn't tell you anything. Look at the next number—hunt around until you find 3, the power to which we are raising the binomial. That row reads 1, 3, 3, 1—the numbers to fill in the blanks we left. Then you have:

$$(b + g)^3 = 1b^3 + 3b^2g + 3bg^2 + 1g^3$$

You are now ready to solve any problem about the number of boys and girls in a family of three. We are looking for two boys and one girl, so take the term that fits this specification—$3b^2g$—and fill in the respective probabilities. (These problems all go on the assumption that the chances are even that a child will be a boy or girl, which is not exactly correct biologically, since there are a few more boys born. However, use $\frac{1}{2}$ as the probability in each case, which is mathematically near enough for the purpose.)

$$3b^2g = 3 \, (\tfrac{1}{2})^2(\tfrac{1}{2}) = 3 \, (\tfrac{1}{4})(\tfrac{1}{2}) = \tfrac{3}{8}$$

There you are with the probability that, in a family of three children, there will be two boys and one girl. For other combinations, just use other terms of the expansion of the binomial $(b + g)^3$.

Three boys: $1b^3 = 1 \, (\tfrac{1}{2})^3 = \tfrac{1}{8}$
One boy and two girls:
$3bg^2 = 3(\tfrac{1}{2})(\tfrac{1}{2})^2 = 3(\tfrac{1}{2})(\tfrac{1}{4}) = \tfrac{3}{8}$
Three girls: $1g^3 = 1(\tfrac{1}{2})^3 = \tfrac{1}{8}$

To check, add the four different probabilities. Since mathematically they cover all the possibilities of the situation, their sum should be one.

$$\tfrac{3}{8} + \tfrac{1}{8} + \tfrac{3}{8} + \tfrac{1}{8} = \tfrac{8}{8} = 1$$

The Chevalier de Méré's problem is of this binomial type. Although there are many ways the dice could fall, for the purposes of his bet they were lumped into two categories—twelve $(t)$ or non-twelve $(n)$. Since he wagered on getting at least one 12 in 24 rolls of the dice, the binomial would have to be raised to the twenty-fourth power. It is no wonder he had to consult two of the most eminent mathematicians of his time—Pascal and Fermat. Furthermore, the probabilities of each term that contained a $t$ would have to be calculated and then added together.

Fortunately, there is a much shorter way. Since the total probability of all the terms is always 1, find the probability that the Chevalier will lose his bet and then take the complement. He loses in only one case—no twelves—so subtract that probability from 1 and you have it.

Most "at least" problems are best done this way, although I don't think your high school son's algebra book will have an example this hard. They usually confine themselves to something like this: The probability of a certain brand of thumbtacks' falling with the point up is $\tfrac{2}{3}$. If three such tacks are tossed simultaneously, what is the probability that at least one will fall point up? (By the way, a single thumbtack tossed three times or three tacks tossed simultaneously are exactly the same problem, provided the tacks are all alike.)

The probability of point up $(u) = \frac{2}{3}$
The probability of point down $(d) = \frac{1}{3}$
$(u + d)^3 = 1u^3 + 3u^2d + 3ud^3 + 1d^3$

The only term which does not contain a $u$ is the last one.

Evaluating: $1d^3 = 1(\frac{1}{3})^3 = \frac{1}{27}$
The complement of this term is: $1 - \frac{1}{27} = \frac{26}{27}$

Therefore the probability that at least one thumbtack will fall point up is $\frac{26}{27}$.

### PROBLEMS

1. If three coins are tossed simultaneously, what is the probability two will be tails and one will be heads?

2. In a family of four children, what is the probability there will be two boys and two girls?

3. A warped coin has the probability of falling heads $\frac{5}{8}$ of the time. If it is tossed three times in succession, what is the probability it will be tails at least once?

4. In problem number 3, what is the probability that it will be heads at least once?

### RANDOM NUMBER TABLES

Public opinion pollsters are not the only ones to use random samples of the population. And population does not necessarily mean people, or even animate creatures. If you wish to sample hay, then the bales comprise the population. Most major industries in this country take random samples to check on the quality of the articles they produce. The technique of insuring randomness in the sample is most important; otherwise the conclusions drawn from it are out of kilter with the true state of affairs in the whole population. It usually requires the selection of numbers in some fashion.

You do not get random numbers simply by jotting down whatever pops into your head because, subconsciously, you will favor certain ones—maybe three or seven or whatever you consider your lucky number. There is some indication that if you say: "Pick a number from one to ten," most people will choose one toward the middle, avoiding the edges, like 1 or 10.

A random number has to be generated by some physical process which will assure that each number has an equal chance of being chosen. You *could* draw slips from a hat or deal cards, but after two or three hours of this, for some large-scale problem, you begin to wish for a shorter, easier method. Furthermore, fatigue leads to poor shuffling, with consequent loss of randomness, and slips are hard to mix properly. (There have been some scientific papers written on the question of whether the capsules used in the draft in World War II were thoroughly stirred in their bowl; or if, in fact, they were still somewhat layered, so that some numbers were more likely to be drawn than others.)

The answer is the random number table. It is quick, simple, and efficient. Besides, it looks considerably more businesslike to be sitting at your desk perusing a table than rolling dice, which could be open to misinterpretation.

In appearance a random number table resembles any other mathematical table, but the numbers don't mean a

thing. You look nothing up by row and column. Start anywhere and read in any direction—it makes no difference.
Here is a short one I made by drawing cards numbered
from 0 through 9 (the numbers are grouped merely for
convenience in reading):

| 81961 | 91798 | 41508 | 72680 |
| 07898 | 93844 | 18687 | 37964 |
| 53739 | 75892 | 48228 | 58327 |
| 37729 | 04625 | 17534 | 20670 |

When you use a random number table you are actually
using the physical process behind it. The table above provides you with numbers as authentically random as if
drawn from cards, but spares you the exertion. They are
much in demand. The Interstate Commerce Commission's
Bureau of Transport Economics and Statistics puts out a
*Table of 105,000 Random Decimal Digits*. The Rand Corporation, which goes in for this sort of thing in a big way,
has a volume called *A Million Random Digits*. The reason
it takes so many is because you use them up, like paper
cups. After you have employed the first fifty, say, for some
experiment, cross them off and don't take those any more.
Otherwise, the same sequence of digits would occur over
and over. Of course, if you want to be economical, you
can go back and use them over, reading in a different direction—vertically this time, if you went horizontally before.

The place you are most likely to encounter a random
number table is in your child's science text. The National
Science Teachers Association puts out a little book, *Experimentation and Measurement*, for use in junior and sen-

ior high school, explaining random selection of samples for measurement in the laboratory.

To give you a little practice in using a random number table, suppose you select five names at random from the telephone book, maybe for a television quiz, using approved scientific methods. (Why can't you just open the book and jab, blindfolded? Because the book will probably open at the pages you use most, therefore each name will not have an equal chance of being chosen.) In most cases, the book will have less than a thousand pages (not counting the yellow section), four colums to a page, and less than a hundred names to the column. Use the table above and, starting anywhere, take three digits in order. That gives you the page. Cross them off and use the next digit for the column number. If it is larger than your number of columns, skip it and go on until you reach a figure that fits. Mark these off, then take the next pair of digits to find the name, counting from the top of the column down. *There* is the lucky person. Do this five times, always using fresh digits, and you have a true random sample of five telephone subscribers in your community.

The random number table can also be a modern device to replace drawing straws, as the Commission on Mathematics text *Introductory Probability and Statistical Inference* explains. Suppose four college girls pool their money and buy a fur jacket, agreeing to take turns wearing it. Joan puts in 10% of the cost, Susan 20%, Jane 30%, and Melinda 40%. On the Saturday of the big game, naturally, they all want to wear it at once. They agree to draw, but the girls who paid more money think they should have a better chance. What to do? Borrow a random number table and assign each girl digits in proportion to her investment. Joan gets one digit, say 0; Susan gets 1,2; Jane gets 3,4,5; and Melinda 6,7,8,9. Open the random number table and read the first digit that is not marked out. Whichever girl has that number gets to wear the jacket—all fair, square, and scientific.

In case the situation doesn't jibe so neatly with the decimal system, the random number table will still work. Suppose three boys buy a boat—John pays ⅛ of the price, Steve pays ⅜, and Bill puts up ⅝. To decide who will get to use it on a given day, make an arrangement like this:

| Number | Winner |
|--------|--------|
| 9 | John |
| 8 | Steve |
| 7 | Steve |
| 6 | Bill |
| 5 | Bill |
| 4 | Bill |
| 3 | Bill |
| 2 | Bill |
| 0,1 | (Skip and go on to the next digit.) |

Each of the eight digits 2 through 9 are equally likely, and each has a probability of ⅛. John's, Steve's, and Bill's chances of winning are exactly the same as the fraction of the cost they paid.

# New Math and Tests   **10**

The next question is: How much of this new math is included in the tests which your child will have to take to gain admission to college? It partly depends, of course, on which college he is applying to.

A great many require the examinations of the College Board. How much has this board changed their exams to jibe with the recommendations of their own Commission on Mathematics? The policy announced in the original report was that they would gradually include new material at the same pace that it was incorporated in the secondary school courses. By studying the booklets describing the tests which they send to each applicant and by questioning high school seniors who have taken the latest exams, it is possible to gauge the extent to which this has taken place. (They long ago discontinued their former practice of selling copies of old exams and of publishing detailed syllabi of the courses tested.) Questions on inequalities and probability, both topics in the new math, are included, but sets are not as yet, although a few problems are couched in characteristic set language, such as:

$$\text{``What are all } x \text{ such that } \frac{2x + 5}{x} \leqq 3?\text{''}$$

—a plainly cast shadow of what is to come.

These are the achievement exams, of which there are

two offered in mathematics—the intermediate, and the advanced.* Since a candidate for college entrance only has to take three out of fourteen exams offered (the choice is not quite free—one has to be in English), he does not necessarily have to take one in math, unless his particular college requires it. But there is no escape, because the Scholastic Aptitude Test, which they all have to take, includes a section on mathematics.

The difference in the two is that an achievement test measures what a student has learned in a certain field, much like a final examination, while an aptitude test is a test of his general ability to understand and solve problems. Specific topics are avoided in the aptitude test. It is not, however, designed just to be a test of his inborn capacity. What they are looking for is a measure of his aptitude for future academic work, and this encompasses both native and acquired ability. In fact, there is no way to divorce the two. The best of tests can only produce scores which reflect the combined influences of heredity and environment.

The recent versions of the Aptitude Test clearly follow the new viewpoint toward mathematics strongly advocated in the commission's report. This point of view holds that a student should search for insights into the nature of a problem, rather than learn a bag of tricks to solve it. He should look for elements in it that resemble problems he already knows how to work, but first he should be able to decide whether there is enough information given to make the problem solvable at all. The inclusion of data-sufficiency questions shows this trend.

* Beginning in December, 1964, these will be replaced by two new tests—Level I (Standard) and Level II (Intensive).

A data-sufficiency problem is something like this: Is the average length of 12 poles greater than 5 feet 5 inches if

1. ½ of the poles are 5 feet 7 inches.
2. ¼ of the poles are 5 feet 4 inches.

You are asked to decide whether statement 1 or statement 2 alone is sufficient to solve the problem; if both statements are necessary for a solution; or if it can't be solved at all from the information given.

Many colleges which do not ask for College Boards require, instead, the examination prepared by the American College Testing Program, an organization with headquarters at Iowa City, Iowa. There is no choice here—all candidates take the same four-part test on English Usage, Mathematics Usage, Social Studies Reading, and Natural Sciences Reading.

Up to now, the problems in their mathematics section have all been from traditional arithmetic, algebra, and geometry, in an effort to restrict the test to material which all the students could reasonably be expected to have had and thus to eliminate subject-matter differences among them. However, this is extremely difficult to do in a mathematics test for use nationally in this transition period when curriculums vary so greatly in content from school to school. It is reasonable to predict that, as mathematics courses change on a national scale, so will the test.

If Susie and Billy are going to try for scholarships to college, they will have to take, in March of their junior year in high school, the National Merit Scholarship Qualifying Test, administered by Science Research Associates. This examination, a three-hour test of educational development, is the first step in the annual competition for four-year scholarships provided by the National Merit Scholarship Corporation and other sponsoring organizations. Out of forty questions on the mathematics section of the latest one, there were three problems in which a knowledge of new math would be of help to the candidate.

High scorers on this examination become semifinalists in the competition and go on to take the College Board Aptitude Test in December of their senior year in high school. If they repeat their high performance, they are then finalists, and the winners are picked from this group. A Merit Scholarship may amount to anywhere from $100 a year to a total of $6,000 for the full four years in college, depending on financial need.

Organizations that make tests for nationwide use in specific grades are in a dilemma during this period of mathematical flux. How can they possibly devise problems to find out whether sixth-graders can add, when who knows, for any given school, what the sixth grade is adding? It may be natural numbers, rational numbers, integers, or, possibly, matrices.

The National Association of Independent Schools, which offers achievement tests for sixth, seventh, eighth, and ninth grades, has tried, as a temporary measure, putting all the new math in an optional section at the end. In 1964 they will replace their two former eighth-grade tests —one on algebra and one largely on arithmetic—with a single new test made up of traditional algebra, heavily interlarded with problems on such new topics as sets, number properties, and inequalities.

The Educational Records Bureau of New York appointed its own Subcommittee on Mathematics which wrote four new tests at the high school level. For the most part the ERB uses tests prepared by other agencies—its services consist of scoring and ranking students' answers against nationwide norms—but in this unusual situation they developed their own. One of the new tests is entirely on probability and statistics, containing problems similar to this:

If four coins are tossed together at random, the probability that all four will fall tails is

1. $\frac{1}{16}$    2. 1    3. $\frac{1}{8}$    4. $\frac{1}{4}$    5. $\frac{3}{8}$

Another of the tests is on sets, equations, inequalities, and number concepts. The questions here are of this type:

If $X \subset Y$, which of the following is always true?
1. $X \cap Y = Y'$
2. $X \cup Y = X'$
3. $X \cap Y = X$
4. $X \cup Y = X$
5. None of the above.

and

Which one of the following statements is true?
1. $-50 > 0$
2. $-\frac{7}{6} < -\frac{7}{5}$
3. $-5 > -3$
4. $-6 < 2$
5. $6 - 8 = 5 + 2$

The ERB gave members a three-way choice. To schools that had departed from the traditional mathematics curriculum to follow the new program they recommended the new tests. To schools that were in the process of revising their courses (by far the most numerous group) they advised the use of the new tests to supplement the old. Schools that had not changed could continue to use the former tests.

These former tests they refer to are the Cooperatives, prepared by the Educational Testing Service of Princeton, New Jersey, who also make the College Board examinations. Like other similar organizations, they speak of "this difficult period of transition and ferment in the mathematics curriculum," at the same time busily constructing tests to fit it. Their new geometry examination was made available in the spring of 1963. It reflected the major shift in that course by including questions on solid and coordinate geometry with those on plane geometry.

They have also prepared new tests in arithmetic and algebra, which will go into use in 1964. Problems on inequalities are found on all these examinations, but sets are not.

In short, with all these major groups at work, there soon won't be any old tests left for schools to continue to use, even in the unlikely event that they should want to.

# Solutions to Problems

<small>Chapter</small> II <small>Sets</small>

*Set Membership*
1. {1,3,5,7,9}
2. {all the days of the week} or {$x \mid x$ is a day of the week}
3. $\phi$
4. circle

*Subsets*
1. 32
2. 12
3. 7
4. {$x,y,z$}, {$x$}, {$y$}, {$z$}, {$x,y$}, {$x,z$}, {$y,z$}, $\phi$
5. True
6. False
7. True

*Set Operations*
1. {4,6}
2. {3,4,5,6,7,9,10}
3. {1,2,3,8,9,10}
4. {3,4,6,9,10}
5. {1,3,8,9,10}
6. {2}
7. $\phi$
8. 1 if $A \neq B$
9. 0
10. $\phi$
11. True
12. True

*Cartesian Product*
1. $\{(2,1), (2,3), (4,1), (4,3), (6,1), (6,3)\}$
2. $\{(1,5), (1,10), (1,15), (1,20)$
   $(2,5), (2,10), (2,15), (2,20)$
   $(3,5), (3,10), (3,15), (3,20)\}$
3. $\{(1,1), (1,2), (1,3), (1,4)$
   $(2,1), (2,2), (2,3), (2,4)$
   $(3,1), (3,2), (3,3), (3,4)$
   $(4,1), (4,2), (4,3), (4,4)\}$

## CHAPTER III NEW ARITHMETICS

*Modulo Five System*
1. 1
2. 4
3. 2
4. 1
5. $x = 1$
6. $x = 4$
7. $x = 1$
8. 9, 14, 19, and others
9. 11, 36, 81, and others
10. 4, and others

*Modulo Ten System*
1. 8
2. 1
3. 2
4.

| + | 0 | 1 | 2 | 3 | 4 | 5 | 6 |
|---|---|---|---|---|---|---|---|
| 0 | 0 | 1 | 2 | 3 | 4 | 5 | 6 |
| 1 | 1 | 2 | 3 | 4 | 5 | 6 | 0 |
| 2 | 2 | 3 | 4 | 5 | 6 | 0 | 1 |
| 3 | 3 | 4 | 5 | 6 | 0 | 1 | 2 |
| 4 | 4 | 5 | 6 | 0 | 1 | 2 | 3 |
| 5 | 5 | 6 | 0 | 1 | 2 | 3 | 4 |
| 6 | 6 | 0 | 1 | 2 | 3 | 4 | 5 |

5.

| × | 0 | 1 | 2 |
|---|---|---|---|
| 0 | 0 | 0 | 0 |
| 1 | 0 | 1 | 2 |
| 2 | 0 | 2 | 1 |

6. 12, 33, 61, and others
7. $x = 2$
8. $x = 2$

*Modulo Six System*
1. $x = 1, 4$
2. $x = 5, 2$
3. $x = 2$
4. 0
5. 5
6. 8, 38, 62, and others

*Binary Arithmetic*
1. 12
2. 10
3. 7
4. 51
5. 124
6. 1100
7. 11100
8. 10110
9. 110001111
10. 11100100

*Other Bases*
1. 85
2. 41
3. 82
4. 1308
5. $333_{five}$
6. $101101_{two}$
7. $125_{twelve}$
8. $1101001_{two}$
9. $645_{eight}$
10. $111010_{two}$

CHAPTER IV NUMBER SYSTEMS

*Natural Numbers*
1. Googol
2. Archimedes' number
3. Googolplex
4. 13th order

### Rational Numbers

1. $\frac{1}{3} + \frac{1}{2}$; $\frac{1}{4} + \frac{1}{2}$; $\frac{1}{2}$; $\frac{1}{3}$; $\frac{1}{3} + \frac{1}{3}$
2. 24
3. $\frac{5}{8}$; $\frac{7}{16}$

### Irrational Numbers

1. 70    99
   169   239
   408   577
2. $\frac{70}{99} = .7070707\ldots$
   $\frac{169}{239} = .7071129707\ldots$
   $\frac{408}{577} = 707105719\ldots$
   $1/\sqrt{2} = .7071068\ldots$
3. $1.414^2 = 1.999396$       $1.415^2 = 2.002225$
   $1.4142^2 = 1.99996$      $1.4143^2 = 2.00024$
   $1.41421^2 = 1.999989$    $1.41422^2 = 2.000018$

### Negative Numbers

1. $6, \sqrt{16}$
2. $\frac{3}{4}, 0, -12, 6\frac{1}{4}, \sqrt{\frac{1}{4}}, -5\frac{1}{2}, (\frac{1}{2} + \frac{1}{4}), (\frac{1}{4} - \frac{1}{2}),$
   $1.32\overline{156}$
3. $6, \sqrt{16}$
4. $\sqrt{5}, -\sqrt{10}, 5 - \sqrt{3}$
5. Same as problem 2

### Complex Numbers

1. $i^2, i^6, -i^4, 2i^8$
2. 13; real

## CHAPTER V PROPERTIES OF NUMBER SYSTEMS

### The ACD Laws and Arithmetic

1. True. Associative and commutative laws for addition
2. False
3. True. Associative law for addition
4. True. Commutative law for multiplication
5. False
6. False
7. True. Associative law for multiplication
8. True. Distributive law
9. False
10. True. Distributive law

*Other Number Properties*
1. $-3, -\frac{1}{2}, -1, 2, \frac{4}{3}$
2. $\frac{1}{3}, 2, 1, -\frac{1}{2}, -\frac{3}{4}$
3. Inverse law for multiplication
4. Identity law for addition
5. Inverse law for addition
6. Identity law for multiplication

*The ACD and Other Laws in Algebra*
1. $(2a + 3b) + (5a + 7b) = (3b + 2a) + (5a + 7b)$
Commutative law
$$= 3b + [2a + (5a + 7b)]$$
Associative law
$$= 3b + [(2a + 5a) + 7b]$$
Associative law
$$= 3b + [7a + 7b] \text{ Dis-tributive law}$$
$$= 3b + (7b + 7a) \text{ Com-mutative law}$$
$$= (3b + 7b) + 7a \text{ Asso-ciative law}$$
$$= 10b + 7a \quad \text{Distributive law}$$
$$= 7a + 10b \text{ Commutative law}$$

2. $ab + ac + ad = (ab + ac) + ad$
$$= a(b + c) + ad \text{ Distributive law}$$
$$= a[(b + c) + d] \text{ Distributive law}$$
$$= a[b + c + d] \quad \text{Definition:}$$
$$(b + c + d) = b + c + d$$

3. $(a + 2b)(2a + b) = [(a + 2b)2a] + [(a + 2b)b]$
Distributive law
$$= [2a(a + 2b)] + [b(a + 2b)]$$
Commutative law
$$= [2a^2 + (2a)(2b)] + [ba + b(2b)]$$

Distributive law

$$= [2a^2 + 4ab] +$$
$$[ab + 2b^2]$$

Commutative and Associative laws for multiplication

$$= 2a^2 + 5ab + 2b^2 \text{ Associative law for addition and definition}$$

*Mathematical Systems*
1. Yes, for all
2. A. Yes  B. No  C. No  D. Yes
3. A. Yes, 0  B. No  C. Yes, 1  D. Yes, $e$
4. A. Yes; the inverse of 2 is 1, the inverse of 0 is 0, the inverse of 1 is 2.
   B. No element has an inverse.
   C. The inverse of 1 is 1. No other element has an inverse.
   D. The inverse of $a$ is $a$, the inverse of $e$ is $e$, the inverse of $b$ is $b$, the inverse of $c$ is $c$.

CHAPTER VI INEQUALITIES

*Graphing the Solution Set on a Number Line*

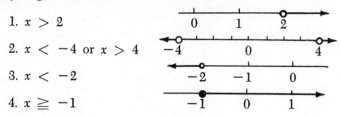

1. $x > 2$
2. $x < -4$ or $x > 4$
3. $x < -2$
4. $x \geqq -1$
5. $x < -7$
6. No solution
7. $x \neq 7$
8. $x > 4$
9. No solution
10. Any number between 0 and 5, inclusive

*Axioms of Inequalities*
1. $x < 3$
2. $x > 2$

3. $x \leqq -1$
4. $x > -3$
5. $x < 1$
6. $x \leqq 5$

*Graphing in a Plane*
1. $x = 11$ (Number of hours for Esperanto)
   $y = 6$ (Number of hours for Early Egyp. Plumb.)

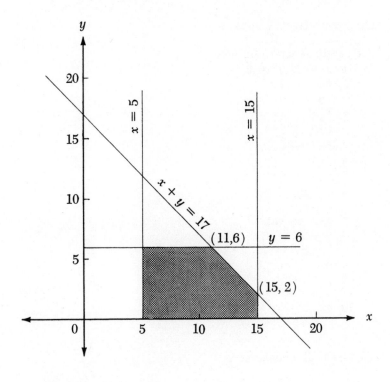

CHAPTER VII GEOMETRY

*Topology*
1. *b*
2. *a*
3. 20

*Other Non-Metric Geometry*
1. 3, non-metric
2. 4, non-metric
3. 50, metric
4. a. real    b. real    c. ideal; non-metric
5. $\dfrac{9\sqrt{3}}{4}$, metric

## CHAPTER VIII MATRICES

*Operations with Matrices*
1. $x = 2, y = 9$
2. $\begin{pmatrix} 4 & 13 \\ 6 & 6 \end{pmatrix}$
3. $\begin{pmatrix} 12 & 6 \\ 10 & 8 \end{pmatrix}$
4. Not possible
5. $\begin{pmatrix} 83 & 4 \\ 35 & 20 \end{pmatrix}$
6. $\begin{pmatrix} -26 & 2 \\ -1 & 3 \end{pmatrix}$
7. Not possible
8. $\begin{pmatrix} -5 & -30 & 40 \\ 2 & 12 & -16 \\ 1 & 6 & -8 \end{pmatrix}$
9. $\begin{pmatrix} 5 & 11 \\ 12 & 8 \end{pmatrix}$
10. 49

## CHAPTER IX PROBABILITY

*Simple Probability*
1. $\frac{1}{7}$
2. $\frac{6}{11}$
3. $\frac{2}{7}$; $\frac{3}{7}$
4. $\frac{1}{2}$
5. 7 to 5; $\frac{7}{12}$

*Compound Probability*

1. $\frac{6}{10}$
2. $\frac{16}{100}$
3. $\frac{1}{4} + \frac{1}{4} - \frac{1}{16} = \frac{7}{16}$
4. $\frac{1}{36}$
5. $\frac{5}{36}$

*Binomial Experiments*

1. $3(\frac{1}{2})^2(\frac{1}{2}) = \frac{3}{8}$
2. $6(\frac{1}{2})^2(\frac{1}{2})^2 = \frac{6}{16}$ or $\frac{3}{8}$
3. $1 - (\frac{5}{8})^3 = 1 - \frac{125}{512} = \frac{387}{512}$
4. $1 - (\frac{3}{8})^3 = 1 - \frac{27}{512} = \frac{485}{512}$

# Bibliography

## CHAPTER II SETS

Aiken, Daymond J., and Beseman, Charles A. *Modern Mathematics*. New York: McGraw-Hill Book Co., 1959.

Allendoerfer, C. B., and Oakley, C. O. *Principles of Mathematics*. New York: McGraw-Hill Book Co., 1955.

College Entrance Examination Board. *Report of the Commission on Mathematics. Appendices*. New York, 1959.

Courant, Richard, and Robbins, Herbert. *What Is Mathematics?* Fair Lawn, N.J.: Oxford University Press, 1941.

Kelley, John L. *Introduction to Modern Algebra*. Princeton, N.J.: D. Van Nostrand Co., 1960.

Krickenberger, W. R., and Pearson, Helen R. *Sets and the Structure of Algebra*. Boston: Ginn and Co., 1958.

National Council of Teachers of Mathematics. *The Growth of Mathematical Ideas*. Washington, D.C., 1959.

## CHAPTER III NEW ARITHMETICS

Adler, Irving. *The New Mathematics*. New York: The John Day Co., 1958.

Allendoerfer, C. B., and Oakley, C. O. *Principles of Mathematics*. New York: McGraw-Hill Book Co., 1955.

Andree, Richard V. *Modern Abstract Algebra*. New York: Holt, Rinehart and Winston, 1958.

Courant, Richard, and Robbins, Herbert. *What Is Mathematics?* Fair Lawn, N.J.: Oxford University Press, 1941.

Vannatta, Glen D., Carnahan, Walter H., and Fawcett, Harold P. *Advanced High School Mathematics*. Columbus, Ohio: Charles E. Merrill Books, 1961.

Vannatta, Glen D., Goodwin, A. Wilson, and Fawcett, Harold P. *Algebra Two, A Modern Course*. Columbus, Ohio: Charles E. Merrill Books, 1962.

CHAPTER IV NUMBER SYSTEMS

Allendoerfer, C. B., and Oakley, C. O. *Principles of Mathematics.*
New York: McGraw-Hill Book Co., 1955.

College Entrance Examination Board. *Report of the Commission on
Mathematics. Appendices.* New York, 1959.

Eves, Howard, and Newsom, Carroll V. *An Introduction to the
Foundations and Fundamental Concepts of Mathematics.* New
York: Rinehart and Co., 1958.

Gamow, George. *One, Two, Three . . . Infinity.* New York: The
Viking Press, 1947.

National Council of Teachers of Mathematics. *The Growth of
Mathematical Ideas.* Washington, D.C., 1959.

Newman, James R. *The World of Mathematics.* New York: Simon
and Schuster, 1956. "The Great Mathematicians" by Turnbull;
"The Rhind Papyrus" by Newman; "Greek Mathematics" by
Thomas; "The Sand Reckoner" by Archimedes.

School Mathematics Study Group. *Report of a Conference on Elementary School Mathematics.* New Haven: Yale University,
1959.

————. *Report of an Orientation Conference for SMSG Elementary
School Experimental Centers.* New Haven: Yale University,
1960.


CHAPTER V PROPERTIES OF NUMBER SYSTEMS

Adler, Irving. *The New Mathematics.* New York: The John Day
Co., 1958.

Allendoerfer, C. B., and Oakley, C. O. *Principles of Mathematics.*
* New York: McGraw-Hill Book Co., 1955.

Andree, Richard V. *Modern Abstract Algebra.* New York: Holt,
Rinehart and Winston, 1958.

Eves, Howard, and Newsom, Carroll V. *An Introduction to the
Foundations and Fundamental Concepts of Mathematics.* New
York: Rinehart and Co., 1958.

Kelley, John L. *Introduction to Modern Algebra.* Princeton, N.J.:
D. Van Nostrand Co., 1960.

School Mathematics Study Group. *Report of a Conference on Elementary School Mathematics.* New Haven: Yale University,
1959.

————. *Report of an Orientation Conference for SMSG Elementary
School Experimental Centers.* New Haven: Yale University,
1960.

————. *Report of an Orientation Conference for SMSG Experimental Centers.* New Haven: Yale University, 1959.

## CHAPTER VI INEQUALITIES

Aiken, Daymond J., and Beseman, Charles A. *Modern Mathematics, Topics and Problems.* New York: McGraw-Hill Book Co., 1959.

College Entrance Examination Board. *Report of the Commission on Mathematics. Appendices.* New York, 1959.

————. *Concepts of Equation and Inequality.* New York, 1958.

Kemeny, John G., Snell, J. Laurie, and Thompson, Gerald L. *Introduction to Finite Mathematics.* Englewood Cliffs, N.J.: Prentice-Hall, Inc., 1956, 1957.

Vannatta, Glen D., Carnahan, Walter H., and Fawcett, Harold P. *Advanced High School Mathematics.* Columbus, Ohio: Charles E. Merrill Books, 1961.

## CHAPTER VII GEOMETRY

College Entrance Examination Board. *Report of the Commission on Mathematics. Appendices.* New York, 1959.

Courant, Richard, and Robbins, Herbert. *What Is Mathematics?* Fair Lawn, N.J.: Oxford University Press, 1941.

Eves, Howard, and Newsom, Carroll V. *An Introduction to the Foundations and Fundamental Concepts of Mathematics.* New York: Rinehart and Co., 1958.

Newman, James R. *The World of Mathematics.* New York: Simon and Schuster, 1956. "Greek Mathematics" by Ivor Thomas; "The Seven Bridges of Königsberg" by Leonhard Euler; "Dürer as a Mathematician" by Erwin Panofsky; "Projective Geometry" by Morris Kline.

School Mathematics Study Group. *Report of a Conference on Elementary School Mathematics.* New Haven: Yale University, 1959.

————. *Report of an Orientation Conference for SMSG Elementary School Experimental Centers.* New Haven: Yale University, 1960.

————. *Report of an Orientation Conference for SMSG Experimental Centers.* New Haven: Yale University, 1959.

CHAPTER VIII MATRICES

Adler, Irving. *The New Mathematics*. New York: The John Day Co., 1958.

Andree, Richard V. *Modern Abstract Algebra*. New York: Holt, Rinehart, and Winston, 1958.

Crouch, Ralph, and Walker, Elbert. *Introduction to Modern Algebra and Analysis*. New York: Holt, Rinehart and Winston, 1962.

Kelley, John L. *Introduction to Modern Algebra*. Princeton, N.J.: D. Van Nostrand Co., 1960.

School Mathematics Study Group. *Introduction to Matrix Algebra*. New Haven: Yale University Press, 1961.


CHAPTER IX PROBABILITY

Allendoerfer, C. B., and Oakley, C. O. *Principles of Mathematics*. New York: McGraw-Hill Book Co., 1955.

Commission on Mathematics. *Introductory Probability and Statistical Inference, An Experimental Course*. New York: College Entrance Examination Board, 1959.

Gamow, George. *One Two Three . . . Infinity*. New York: The Viking Press, 1947.

Huff, Darrell. *How to Take a Chance*. New York: W. W. Norton and Co., 1959.

Krickenberger, W. R., and Pearson, Helen R. *Sets and the Structure of Algebra*. Boston: Ginn and Co., 1958.

National Council of Teachers of Mathematics. *The Growth of Mathematical Ideas*. Washington, D.C., 1959.

Youden, W. J. *Experimentation and Measurement*. Washington, D.C.: National Science Teachers Association, 1962.

# Index